C000000790

"*Last Rights* is a humane, sensible argument for changing the law on assisted dying, a moral issue whose time has come. All parliamentarians should consider the points raised in this book and question why we have abrogated our responsibility to change the law for so long."

THE RIGHT HONOURABLE BARONESS BETTY BOOTHROYD OM

"If we care about the way we live we should also care about the way we die, yet we run away from the issue. We need to talk about it, and to decide. This book harnesses both passion and insight to pursue a very important cause."

MICHAEL DOBBS, AUTHOR OF *HOUSE OF CARDS*

"This deeply humane book presents a brilliant, impassioned, carefully argued and indeed unanswerable case for the long-overdue legalisation of assisted dying. Above all, it exposes the cruelty and irrationality of the present law. *Last Rights* should be read by legislators, by physicians and by those whom this issue will affect – that is to say all of us."

RAY TALLIS, PHILOSOPHER AND EMERITUS PROFESSOR OF GERIATRIC MEDICINE

"Modern medicine makes it possible to live longer lives, but we will all die. We want death to be pain-free and calm, with our loved ones at our side, but the reality for some dying people is one of prolonged suffering and distress. *Last Rights* demonstrates that we can do much better for dying people. How? We must change the law on assisted dying and change our culture so that dying people have real power to decide on the death they want."

JOAN BAKEWELL

"The moral (and, for me, the Christian) case for a change in the law is irrefutable. Covid-19 has forced us all to rethink our certainties about death and dying. How can a country that cares so deeply for victims of this virus be so indifferent to those who, at the end of life, suffer indignity and intractable pain? Sarah Wootton and Lloyd Riley make a timely and powerful case for assisted dying."

LORD CAREY OF CLIFTON, ARCHBISHOP
OF CANTERBURY 1991–2002

"We pride ourselves on our freedom to control our own lives. Yet we are not allowed to control our departure when our suffering is unbearable. There must be a proper inquiry into this ultimate denial of basic human rights. This book makes a powerful case for it."

JOHN HUMPHRYS

"The right to die on our own terms is the last frontier in a long battle to take control of our own beings, our bodies, our life and death. As we continue to grapple with a pandemic that has brought our own mortality centre stage, *Last Rights* makes an urgent, thoughtful case for why now is the time for the victory of compassion and kindness over the cowardice and dogma that prop up the status quo."

POLLY TOYNBEE

"*Last Rights* is a much-needed contribution to the conversation that we must all start to have about dying. In a society that talks so much about human rights, so many forget that one of the most fundamental human rights must surely be an individual's right to choose when and how they die."

JULIA HARTLEY-BREWER

"I cannot think of a better time to publish this vitally important book, which makes a compelling case for changing the outdated, harsh laws that prevent us from having any choice as to how we die, and any hope of a compassionate death."

DAME CARMEN CALLIL, PUBLISHER AND WRITER

"*Last Rights* is a powerful reminder that choice at the end of life is only accessible to those with the money to travel to Switzerland or the means to take matters into their own hands. Fifty years ago, society recognised that forcing women to endure the trauma of a backstreet abortion was unacceptable; the time has now come for us to show the same compassion to dying people."

DIANA MELLY, AUTHOR AND CAMPAIGNER

"Supporters of assisted dying come from all walks of life but are united in deprecating the cruelty and suffering arising from the current law and united in the belief that the autonomy of dying people is a value worth fighting for. This book provides both a serious challenge to the establishment that has resisted law change to date and a rallying call to the compassionate majority."

RABBI DANNY RICH, CHIEF EXECUTIVE, LIBERAL JUDAISM 2004–20

"I am a disability rights advocate. I am also a religious person. Because of these commitments, not despite them, I support the option of assisted dying as a choice for those who are terminally ill. You are free to ignore me, but I do not think you are free to ignore this book."

TOM SHAKESPEARE FBA, PROFESSOR OF DISABILITY RESEARCH, LONDON SCHOOL OF HYGIENE AND TROPICAL MEDICINE

LAST RIGHTS

PROVOCATIONS

LAST RIGHTS
THE CASE FOR ASSISTED DYING

SARAH WOOTTON AND LLOYD RILEY

SERIES EDITOR:

YASMIN ALIBHAI-BROWN

Biteback Publishing

First published in Great Britain in 2020 by
Biteback Publishing Ltd, London
Copyright © Sarah Wootton and Lloyd Riley 2020

ISBN 978-1-78590-601-5

10 9 8 7 6 5 4 3 2

A CIP catalogue record for this book is available from the British Library.

Set in Stempel Garamond

Printed and bound in Great Britain by
CPI Group (UK) Ltd, Croydon CR0 4YY

'You have enemies? Good. That means you've stood up for something, sometime in your life.'

WINSTON CHURCHILL

Contents

Acknowledgements

WHEN WE LOOK back at the history of our movement and the people involved in it, we will remember them as we do the suffragettes who suffered so that future generations of women could have the vote, the Stonewall rioters who led the way in reforming LGBT rights, the women in Ireland who told their stories in order to repeal the Eighth Amendment, and all those who have stood up and spoken out to make things better for those who come after them.

When we have changed the law – and we will change this broken law – we will look back on our supporters and salute their candour and courage. We will all owe them a great debt.

Thank you to every person who has spoken out to

demand an assisted dying law. We will continue to fight for you until our laws are fixed.

Sarah, Lloyd and all of the team at Dignity in Dying

What we believe in

DIGNITY IN DYING campaigns for a law that would give people who are terminally ill and in the final months of their life the option of dying on their own terms.

The law we propose would contain stringent safeguards to protect people. It would only be accessible to mentally competent adults. Two doctors would assess the person making the request to ensure they met the eligibility criteria of the law, and they would explain all other available care options. A High Court judge would examine the person's request and ensure it was being made voluntarily, free from any pressure or coercion. Once a request was approved, a doctor would be able to prescribe life-ending medication for the person, who would then take it themselves under the supervision of a doctor or other healthcare professional.

Dignity in Dying does not campaign for euthanasia, where a doctor might actively end a person's life. Nor do we campaign to provide assisted dying to those who aren't already facing an imminent death.

Under our assisted dying law, healthcare professionals who wanted to conscientiously object would be able to do so. There would be clear reporting procedures for doctors as well as monitoring and annual reports published by the government.

This proposed law is based on one that has operated in Oregon, USA, for twenty-three years, though with additional safeguards built in to make it practical for the UK. There have been no cases of abuse of Oregon's law and no extension of its eligibility criteria. This model of assisted dying legislation has since been adopted in nine other American states and passed by lawmakers in Australia and New Zealand.

Foreword by
Daniel Finkelstein

LOOK AT WHAT we've been ready to do. We've shut ourselves in our homes for months on end. We've not seen our friends and been cut off from our families. Our businesses have closed down and we've let them. We've borrowed billions of pounds to help prop things up, but we know that one day we will have to pay it back.

Our children have been sent home from school or from college. It's sunny outside but they can't see their mates. I am writing this on the table in the lounge because I can't go to the office.

So this is what we've been ready to do. And willingly, too. Almost every one of us, willingly.

Because, you see, we care about life and about suffering and about grief and we will do what we can to prevent it. So much is said about how our bonds have dissolved, that we are now too selfish or too materialistic to see beyond ourselves. But it turns out we aren't.

We look out for each other. We have each other's back. That's the sort of people we are. We've learned something about ourselves, I think. Something good.

So if we are prepared to do something so big to relieve suffering, if we are prepared to sacrifice so much, well then I believe we can do something tiny too.

For that's what the change proposed in this short book is. Tiny. But mighty in its effect. Like the smallest shift of the longest lever.

The campaign for assisted dying seeks the right of terminally ill people to end their life with the help of their doctors. That's all. It's a small step but it would mean so much to so many. And one day it could mean so much to you. Or to someone you love.

People can take their own lives; they've been able to do that since the Conservative government in 1961 introduced the Suicide Act. Suicide used to be illegal once, can you believe that? If you tried to kill yourself and failed, you might well get arrested. Imagine that.

Well, perhaps you don't need to use all that much imagination because now if you help a terminally ill relative die as they wish to, you might well get arrested. And charged, and sentenced.

People still do it, of course, because we have such a strong urge to help the suffering, especially if they are close to us. But if they do, they know they face not only the possibility of criminal sanction but the certainty of criminal investigation.

So this proposal, this small step, is one taken from the shadow of legal uncertainty into the sunlight and firm ground of clear rights and duties.

Now there would be no ambiguity and no needless suffering for the patient or their family. There would be, instead, professional support, careful inquiry, medical advice.

I'm always grimly amused when opponents of assisted dying laws claim that now we have protection for the vulnerable from coercion and a new law would remove it. Can't they see that the opposite is the case? That clear law protects the vulnerable? That if there is any question of coercion, it is better it be identified in advance and prevented rather than identified after someone is dead? A suboptimal moment, to say the least.

So let me address myself, finally, to the government.

I do understand the Conservative way of looking at things. Resistance to unnecessary change, fondness for the settled way, respect for generations of habit and practice.

But the great strength of Conservatives is the ability to understand the moment when the need for change has come. This has allowed Tory governments to implement audacious reforms and accommodate small ones.

This reform is the settled will of the people. It is supported by more than 80 per cent of voters. It has enjoyed this sort of overwhelming backing for decades.

It extends to all citizens, the security and certainty of the law and a choice over the way they deal with their death. What could be more Conservative than that?

For Boris Johnson, this could be a signature reform. One that reaches across liberal Britain and enjoys support even amongst some of the most culturally conservative. One that chimes with the mood of the time.

One that allows the Prime Minister to show that his personal experience and understanding of the mood of the country come together. That tells the vulnerable and the suffering that he gets it.

So why not do this? Why not start now with a review of the Suicide Act 1961, with an inquiry?

All those years ago, a Conservative government could see that the law against suicide was unconscionable. And we can see now that they were right. Time for the next move forward. Well past time, actually.

You can see that, Mr Johnson, can't you?

Prologue

ITV News, 21 January 2020

'I said, "We're doing it today, but you've got to tell me what to do." He said, "Do you mean it, Mavis?" I kissed him on the forehead and said, "Goodnight, God bless, my darling," and he said the same to me.'

'Why was it so important for you?'

'Because I'd promised him. We never broke a promise. We were always truthful to one another.'

'If he had known what you ended up going through…'

'He wouldn't have asked me.'

'Do you have any regrets?'

'No. I'd do the same again. I'd do the same again for my husband. I'd do anything to get him out of the pain.'

In September 2019, a jury at Stafford Crown Court found Mavis Eccleston not guilty of murder or manslaughter. In February 2018, Mavis had helped her husband Dennis take an overdose of pain medication, which he had been prescribed to manage the symptoms of his terminal bowel cancer.

Dennis, 81, wanted to escape his suffering. He found the dying process distressing and undignified. Mavis, 80, was not prepared to live without her husband of nearly sixty years and also tried to end her life. They were found unconscious by family members and taken to hospital. Mavis survived but Dennis died after doctors were notified of his wishes not to be resuscitated. Hospital staff placed their beds together so they could hold hands one last time.

Mavis told nurses that she had helped her husband to die. The nurses notified the police and told her children that their mother was likely to go to prison 'for a long, long time'. Mavis was then arrested and kept in a police cell for thirty hours, still wearing her hospital gown and slippers. The Crown Prosecution Service later said that they had examined the evidence and concluded that it *was* in the public interest to prosecute her.

Reading a statement outside court on the day Mavis was acquitted, over eighteen months later, Mavis and Dennis's daughter Joy said that the Eccleston family had been through a terrible ordeal, worrying that having lost their dad to cancer they might now see their mum imprisoned.

❖ ❖ ❖

A year before Dennis's death, nearly 5,000 miles away in the city of Portland, Oregon, Francie and Charlie Emerick, married for sixty-six years, died peacefully in their sleep thirty minutes apart.

Francie, 88, was finding her struggle with heart disease increasingly difficult. Charlie, 87, had been diagnosed with prostate cancer and Parkinson's disease. They were both dying and took medication knowing it would end their lives.

Francie and Charlie had each been approved for an

assisted death under Oregon's Death with Dignity Act. They had both been independently assessed by two doctors to confirm that they met the clear eligibility criteria set out in Oregon's law.

Six days before they died Francie and Charlie had arranged a family celebration with their children and grandchildren; an opportunity for them to grieve openly and say goodbye. 'We're so glad nobody is telling us we can't do this,' Francie said.

Their daughter Sher made a film of her parents' final days, *Living & Dying: A Love Story*. In the film, Sher explains that her parents' goal was 'to help people change the way they think about dying'. The film shows Francie and Charlie holding hands just moments before they died.

*   *   *

There are many similarities between these two stories. Two couples in their eighties had made a choice to die on their own terms. Both couples loved each other. Both were loved by their families. Both regretted their declining health but knew that they had created happy memories and lived their lives to the full.

There was, however, one key difference. Francie and Charlie, like over 150 million other people around the world, lived in a jurisdiction where choice at the end of life is legal for terminally ill people. They had access to a law that empowered them, while offering protection to themselves, their family, their doctors and others in society. Living in the UK, Dennis was forced to seek an unsafe and unregulated means of control behind closed doors, a choice that unwittingly led to eighteen months of pain for his family. While Mavis was not dying herself, an assisted dying law would have enabled the couple to have an open and honest conversation with Dennis's doctors about his possible options. Things would have been so different for them both.

In Oregon, and many other places around the world, compassion is built into the law. In the UK, compassion is treated as a crime.

Why?

Part I

Who decides how you die?

WHAT WE HAVE witnessed in 2020, what we have all been a part of, is a population forced to confront its own mortality. A deadly pathogen has infected our lives, resulting in fear, panic and a yearning for honesty, clarity and reassurance. We have all become acutely aware of what has slipped out of our control: our health, our finances, our relationships with other people and the world around us. We have had to learn to adjust to the presence of the ominous spaces those things have left behind. We have had to reassess our sense of self and find a way to walk forwards into a dark, indeterminate future.

People who are facing death know what this feels like. They have, for a long time, told us about the physical and existential distress these feelings cause and the tools they need in order to mitigate them. They have told us how empowerment can temper chaos and how choice can be an antidote to uncertainty. We have not been listening to them.

We were not able to stop coronavirus (Covid-19) entering our lives or to prevent the destruction it left in its wake, just as people diagnosed with an aggressive cancer or motor neurone disease or any other terminal condition cannot simply wish their new circumstances away. Yet, like most dying people, we could have been better prepared and better armed to face this new reality, not just with more resources, more knowledge or a refined plan but with the means to navigate death and dying in a fundamentally more sophisticated way.

For many people, the challenge now is to find a way to piece back together their shattered lives, to overcome loss and grief that were forced upon them in the most alien of circumstances, to find a way to stay afloat in times of economic adversity. For others, this might be a time to reflect on the fortuitous circumstances which enabled them to emerge from the storm unharmed, though few will be able to claim they are unchanged.

Some will be anxiously wondering if the storm has passed, if it will return, or if another will soon appear on the horizon. The task that awaits society as a whole is to make sense of what happened and ensure we use it as a platform to improve the world we live in. To do this, we should begin at the end. There has never been a better time for ambitious reform of dying in this country.

The case put forward here to challenge the norms that govern how we die in this country was established long before coronavirus entered the world's consciousness. Indeed, many of the arguments that follow were written when the virus was a misunderstood problem on the other side of the world, too distant and abstract to cause us harm. After all, what more proof did we need that our relationship with dying was already broken than the fact that Mavis Eccleston, a woman guilty only of compassion, was put on trial for murder? Yet set against the backdrop of a society for ever altered by the dramatic events that rapidly unfolded in the first half of 2020, these arguments are stronger, the failings of our present laws and culture around death and dying starker, and the need for radical reform more urgent than ever.

The coronavirus pandemic has thrust death and dying into the mainstream. If there were ever a way to undermine the tired cliché that these are taboo subjects, it was to witness government officials announce the new death toll at 5 p.m. every day. And we all watched, and we discussed the implications of what they said. We didn't close our eyes. We are now discussing our mortality more than ever, but are those discussions frank, honest and capable of enabling us to have the deaths we want to have?

This unfamiliar territory that we now find ourselves in has exposed everything that is wrong with our relationship with dying. Clinicians have inherited a near-monopoly on decision-making at the end of life, a status quo that assumes they will decide *for* people rather than *with* them. There is limited space for people to speak openly about how they want to die, and this has left a vacuum in which a moral and ethical fudge around end-of-life treatment and choice has manifested itself. Why have we not listened to dying people? Why are the norms of medical practice not constructed around their needs and preferences? We need to examine where we are now and how we got here, and we need to question why people have not been equipped with the tools they need to navigate dying on their own terms.

What dying people are telling us reveals their profound wish for a fairer society, one that includes assisted dying law reform.

Lessons from the past

The most remarkable thing about social change is how often the transition between the past and the present appears so seamless in retrospect. Women's suffrage. The civil rights movement. Equal marriage. It is sometimes easy to overlook the fact that people had to fight for these things to be recognised as valid concerns, let alone force them to be written into our statute books. History has been kind to those pioneers.

By contrast, time weathers hypothetical, fear-based arguments until they disintegrate, along with the credibility of those who promoted them. So misguided were the opponents of changes we now take for granted that sometimes we can look back at the bleak, almost laughable fragility of the cases they constructed to oppose them.

Some people in America feared that granting freedom to black people might one day result in a black legislator. Politicians still argue against equal marriage legislation on the basis that allowing people to marry someone of their own sex will inevitably lead to people marrying other species. A concern raised around giving women the vote in Britain was that it would make us seem weak in comparison to our less enlightened colonial rivals, as if it were better to join a race to the bottom than to lead others to a better place.

The argument for assisted dying is one that history will be kind to. Like those debates of the past, the case for assisted dying has the force of morality at its heart, flanked by an arsenal of irrefutable, evidence-based logic. And when change comes it will not be a result of top-down dictum; it will be a reaction to a growing, unstoppable grassroots movement.

In addition to Dignity in Dying's committed team and our legion of dedicated supporters, there is a sense of inevitability driving this campaign forward, one that has provided great comfort in moments of defeat. When MPs last voted against an assisted dying bill in 2015, we remember a friend and fellow campaigner from the USA

contacting us to tell us that the same day, they had suc-
ceeded in passing a piece of legislation in the Californian
state senate. It was their tenth attempt. 'You only have
to win once,' she told us.

Future generations will look back in astonishment at
the horror we subjected dying people to. They will read
accounts of bereaved relatives and question why succes-
sive parliaments failed to act; why respected institutions
insisted our broken law was adequate, paying no attention to the ever-growing evidence that proved otherwise;
why the voices of dying people were repeatedly ignored.

Denying people the option to relieve their own suffering at the end of life will be viewed as just as barbaric and
nonsensical as withholding pain relief during childbirth,
a policy that both the Church of England and many
in the medical professions once advocated. It wasn't
until Queen Victoria demanded pain relief during the
birth of Prince Leopold that objections began to fade
away. Now, while problems still remain, we expect the
experience of childbirth to be a partnership between clinicians and pregnant women. People are given a choice
over when, where and how they will give birth. Births

are not prescribed by doctors; they are curated. This is what dying should look like.

The debate around assisted dying has evolved in recent years. 'Those who do not move, do not notice their chains.' This quote is often attributed to Rosa Luxemburg. Whatever its origins, we believe it to be true. Chains have been placed on dying people subtly, over many years, without their consent. But end-of-life care is moving on and people are beginning to identify contradictions and injustices. They are told their care should be tailored to them, that they should be in control and free to make decisions. Yet they are still being denied ultimate control over how they die. Dying people are moving and they can feel their chains.

This is spilling over into wider society. The tone of our conversations with politicians is shifting. Whereas once this issue was seen as too divisive, it is now seen as something that sooner or later must be addressed. Whereas once we had to seek out those who we suspected had the compassion and vision required to support our campaign, people now come to us. They want to be convinced. The brave individuals who have shared their stories publicly have shown them the cruelty of the current law. They want to help those who suffer. They want to be armed with the evidence that sits behind our campaign: the facts, figures and reassurances that we have gathered from the countries around the world that are way ahead of us.

As with women's suffrage, equal marriage and all other changes that grant freedoms, the benefits of assisted dying will be practical and immediate for those who make use of the law, but it will symbolise something greater. It will tell people that they can have control in their lives, from beginning to end. It will signify that the era of medical paternalism is drawing to a close. Doctors will no longer be able to claim they know best about the most personal and intimate decisions a dying person can make.

In the UK, the campaign to legalise assisted dying dates back, through various guises, to 1935. According to reports, the first ever meeting of the Voluntary Euthanasia Society (VES), the ancestor of Dignity in Dying's campaign, was held at the headquarters of the British Medical Association; it was disrupted by protesters from a Catholic youth organisation.[1]

1 'Doctors urge mercy death be legalised', *Rochester Journal*, 11 December 1935, p. 65.

Throughout most of the twentieth century, the campaign could be considered ahead of its time. The idea that the preferences of a dying person should carry more (or even the same) weight as the expert medical opinions of doctors was inconceivable.

Ironically, assisted dying wasn't explicitly illegal then, though it would have likely been treated as such should cases have made it to court. Suicide was illegal (hence the origin of the anachronistic and insensitive term 'commit suicide', as if it remains a crime that could be committed). An illogical legal quirk was created in 1961 when suicide was decriminalised by Section 1 of the Suicide Act 1961, while Section 2 of that Act criminalised any assistance.

Suicide Act 1961: Section 2

Criminal liability for complicity in another's suicide.

(1) A person ('D') commits an offence if—

(a) D does an act capable of encouraging or assisting the suicide or attempted suicide of another person, and

(b) D's act was intended to encourage or assist suicide or an attempt at suicide.

Many people struggle with the fact that under this law, in England and Wales we now criminalise people for assisting another person to do something that is not in itself illegal.

In Scotland, there is no specific offence of assisting or encouraging suicide, but if there was suspicion that a suicide had been assisted then it would likely be considered a crime under homicide law. In Northern Ireland, a law was passed in 1966 which mirrored the 1961 Suicide Act. Similar provisions exist in the Crown dependencies of Jersey, Guernsey and the Isle of Man.

While much has changed since 1961, Section 2 of the Suicide Act in England and Wales, and the similar legislation elsewhere in the UK, has endured.

In many ways this debate is about power and who holds it. Ultimately, as long as they remain etched into law, true power lies in those few short sentences of legislation above. This law has the power to determine how people die and, by forbidding compassionate assistance at the end of life, it has resulted in the unimaginable suffering of hundreds of thousands of dying people.

Gatekeepers

While this archaic piece of legislation of ours has remained intact, there have been significant developments in how we die.

We are now familiar with the concept of person-centred care, where people are treated (or not treated) in a way that aligns with their attitudes and values. The campaign for greater choice at the end of life once floated in an ether removed from mainstream medical discourse. Over time it has fought its way into the centre of it. Nothing embodies the ideals of person-centred care more than giving dying people the choice, control and freedom they are asking for.

It may once have seemed radical to believe that dying people should be able to relieve their suffering in a manner and at a time of their choosing. Now that view is held by over 80 per cent of people in the UK. Support for assisted dying cuts across political allegiances, gender, class, geography and age. Just as those who were imprisoned for being gay might have scoffed at the thought that one day equal marriage would be legalised, perhaps the ancestors of our cause would be stunned at how much medical culture has evolved to emulate the values enshrined within the assisted dying campaign.

The development of care specifically tailored to dying people was never a core part of the services provided by the NHS. Throughout the 1950s and '60s, Dame Cicely Saunders pioneered treatments for cancer and, later, other terminal diseases. This became what we now know as palliative care, or palliative medicine (palliative is derived from the Latin word *palliare*, which loosely translates as 'to cloak').

Central to the foundations of the hospice movement, and still a core tenet of palliative care, is the idea of 'total pain'. This demands holistic care of dying people, relieving not only their physical suffering but also their social, psychological and spiritual pain.

Saunders was a convert to evangelical Christianity and the specialty she shaped inherited many characteristics of her faith. The very idea of suffering was taken out of the hands of the people who were dying and viewed as the responsibility of caregivers. 'Suffering is only intolerable when nobody cares,' Saunders said, adding, 'One continually sees that faith in God and His care is made infinitely easier by faith in someone who has shown kindness and sympathy.'[2] Not every doctor practising palliative care need view dying through the lens of Christianity, but research shows that palliative care doctors are more likely to identify as Christian than those of other specialties, and religion is shown to be an influencing factor in doctors' decision-making during end-of-life care.[3]

For most of the latter half of the twentieth century, Britain led the way in how Western societies cared for dying people. The progress that Saunders made in such a short space of time and the impact her vision has had around the world are remarkable. In the UK, the specialty of palliative care has expanded, but it is still under-resourced and often under-appreciated. There are now over 200 hospices in this country supporting over 200,000 people each year, yet hospices receive only around a third of their funds from the government. Their sustainability instead depends on the generosity of the

---

2　Paul Brand and Philip Yancey, *The Gift of Pain: Why We Hurt & What We Can Do About It* (Michigan: Zondervan, 1997).

3　'The role of doctors' religious faith and ethnicity in taking ethically controversial decisions during end-of-life care', *Journal of Medical Ethics* (2010), vol. 36, no. 11, pp. 667–82.

communities they serve. This is wrong and government funding of palliative care should be increased.

A common argument against assisted dying is that the greater priority is to further develop palliative care services and so that should be where we focus our efforts. We're not willing to let this debate be reduced to an either/or choice in this way.

Firstly, no matter how good the care is, some people will suffer unbearably as they die. Dignity in Dying has always called and will continue to call for every dying person to have access to the very best care. But we can't put this forward as an all-encompassing fix when we know it won't eradicate intolerable deaths.

Secondly, given many people do acknowledge the limits of palliative care, we question the ethics of holding hostage a small but significant group of dying people (those who will suffer regardless of the care they receive) until a medical specialty gets appropriate resources. Surely, if our compassion is being directed effectively, we should seek to address both of these problems urgently and simultaneously, just as every other society that has grasped this nettle has done.

Why should we accept unnecessary suffering, suffering like Emil's mum was forced to endure?

She was diagnosed when she was 50. It started off as thyroid cancer then spread. She was extremely brave; extremely brave. She went through so many different horrible treatments.

Medical professionals will say that the care that's now out there is amazing, and it lets you die peacefully and keeps you out of pain, which in some cases it probably does – but not in all cases. Because of the complexity of her illness, my mum was suffering all the way to the end.

It grew into her waterworks and she couldn't pee, yet she needed to, and she had bladder spasms so they were forcefully inserting catheters. And there was me, outside the room, hearing her screaming. There was blood everywhere because they didn't know what else to do. They would try to force it in and then the cancer would either reject it or bypass it so that she would still not be able to pass urine. So she had this urge to go – and it just never stopped. That carried on despite medication.

She was in so much distress, despite the medication,

and I was telling the doctors, 'Can you please increase the morphine?' And they said, 'We need to be careful, because if we give her too much morphine and she passes away, it could be looked at as the cause of death.' She was looking at us and saying, 'Why can I not die? If I had known it was going to be like this I would have gone to Switzerland.'

In the end, her symptoms were so distressing they couldn't manage them, so they upped the medication to the point that she was so high, I would say she was clinically dead by then…

My mum didn't want that suffering and that's haunting me. It will haunt me to the end of my life.[4]

Recent surveys carried out by medical Royal Colleges and others show that most doctors do not oppose law change on assisted dying, with the trend showing growing levels of support for it. The latest survey by the Royal College of GPs shows a dramatic shift in opinion in just six years, with support for the college's

---

4 'The True Cost: How the UK outsources death to Dignitas', Dignity in Dying, 2017.

policy of opposition falling from 77 per cent to just 46 per cent. Sadly, it is true that doctors who specialise in palliative care are more likely to oppose assisted dying than their colleagues. When the Royal College of Physicians surveyed its members in 2019, just 43 per cent of respondents wanted their college to oppose law change, yet this figure was over 80 per cent for palliative care doctors.[5] The Association for Palliative Medicine (APM), the representative body for palliative care doctors, was a founding member of the faith-based alliance Care Not Killing and is one of the most active and vocal groups campaigning against a change in the law. The APM's 2019 position statement on assisted dying proclaims that the practice is 'morally and clinically unacceptable'.[6]

While we should acknowledge that just 600 of the UK's 300,000 doctors specialise in palliative care, the apparent strength of feeling amongst these doctors, or

5   'Press release: No majority view on assisted dying moves RCP position to neutral', Royal College of Physicians, March 2019.

6   'Position Statement: Physician Assisted Suicide (sometimes referred to as "Assisted Dying")', Association for Palliative Medicine of Great Britain and Ireland, 2019.

at least the body that represents them, warrants closer examination. We don't accept the argument that the doctors who encounter death more frequently than others have superior insight into this issue, because we know that dying people have the greatest understanding of what it is like to face death, and the vast majority of them want the law to change.[7]

Arguably, it is unsurprising that a specialty that grew in such a short space of time, under the leadership of such an inspiring and determined character, is now out of touch on assisted dying, harbouring objections to a change that most in society now want to see. Time changes all things; elements of a philosophy of death and dying developed in the 1960s may once have been innovative but may now be anachronistic.

Paternalism in end-of-life care has donned numerous guises. Historically, before there were specialists caring for dying people, family doctors would visit people as they died at home, usually from short, aggressive diseases we have since found cures for. Pain relief would be

7   'What Matters to Me: People with terminal and advanced illness on end-of-life choices', Dignity in Dying, 2019.

administered in whatever dosage was deemed necessary. This practice continued well into the 1900s. Everybody has an anecdote about a parent, grandparent or slightly more distant relative who died shortly after a reassuring nod and a wink from the doctor: 'Can you do anything? Can you make them comfortable?' a concerned family member asks. 'Don't worry,' the doctor replies, 'she won't suffer.'

As society has advanced, once-fatal diseases have become treatable, meaning we now live longer, but with lengthier periods of decline in our health. Medicine has dramatically increased the quantity of life in people who would once have died much earlier, while quality of life has struggled to keep pace. This has resulted in people being cared for more in hospitals and care homes, and a relatively quick death at home is harder to achieve.

Running parallel with these changes in how we die has been the expansion of individual rights enshrined in law and also in culture. We naturally yearn for freedom and autonomy in our lives, and the more that is granted, the easier it is to identify areas where freedoms are still unjustifiably restricted. In this context it is unsurprising that tensions arise between doctors and their patients, particularly at the end of life when the magnitude of treatment decisions is drawn into sharp focus. Does the current opposition of palliative care doctors to assisted dying indicate where tensions are the most acute? After all, these are the doctors who have come to wield the most power, because we look to them to control the most feared parts of life: suffering and dying. Even sub-consciously, this power may be difficult to relinquish.

In recent years, people have begun to speak out from within the palliative care community. Five consultants wrote anonymously in the *BMJ*, one of the world's leading medical journals, that palliative care doctors fear speaking out in support of assisted dying because of the threat to their careers.[8] The outgoing APM president confirmed the validity of these concerns and said that he had been ostracised by his own executive committee for advocating a more balanced approach to the debate.[9]

This is a profession that watches over public discourse

---

8   'We risk our careers if we discuss assisted dying, say UK palliative care con-
    sultants', *BMJ* (2019), doi: https://doi.org/10.1136/bmj.l1494.
9   'Assisted dying: The APM should embrace diversity of opinion and encour-
    age sociable debate', *BMJ* (2019), doi: https://doi.org/10.1136/bmj.l1969.

around death and dying, as St Peter guards the Pearly Gates, yet it appears to be fragmented, straining under the forces of contradiction that exist between paternalism and patient choice. The ultimate victims of this tension are not the doctors involved in these disputes but dying people and their families. They are the ones who continue to suffer within a healthcare service that's undergoing something of an identity crisis.

The writer Paulo Coelho once recognised that 'if you want to control someone, all you have to do is to make them feel afraid'. It's an age-old tactic, one that has been used in ominous ways throughout history to suppress truth and to stop people speaking out about causes they believe in. Parallels can be drawn with those doctors who feel afraid of expressing a view that dissents from what a palliative care doctor is supposed to believe.

This would not be unheard of within medicine. In Daphne Romney QC's 2019 report into sexism at the BMA, she found that:

Sex discrimination and sexual harassment are but two aspects of the problematic culture at the BMA. There is also a culture of intolerance of other views. This is seen in some committees, and on list servers, and it stems from an inability on the part of some doctors to concede that there is a point of view other than their own. Some doctors continue to bully and to harass other doctors and staff for reasons other than sex – sometimes it is 'otherism', sometimes it is just bullying and harassment, and sometimes it is a mixture of the two. Whatever it is, it is intolerable, but it has been tolerated and it is poisonous.[10]

Of course, exploring the inner workings of objections to choice at the end of life is not to diminish in any way the incredible dedication of individual doctors, nor the benevolence with which they provide their care. Coronavirus has driven home the astonishing efforts doctors (and all those working in health and social care) make to protect us, and we should never forget that many have tragically died caring for others in the pandemic. But this should not lead us to shy away from difficult questions, and it is reasonable to suggest that

---

10 Daphne Romney QC, 'Independent Report into Sexism at the BMA, British Medical Association', British Medical Association, 2019, para 54.

the culture of medicine bequeathed to doctors working with dying people has not evolved in line with the expansion of individual rights in the rest of society.

In 2019, we published a report detailing the limits of palliative care, 'The Inescapable Truth: How seventeen people a day will suffer as they die'.[11] In the report, we shared stories such as Susan Strong's. Susan's daughter, Fiona, was thirty-one when she died from a rare form of cancer. Fiona was being cared for in a hospice. When doctors concluded she didn't have long to live, they offered to sedate Fiona until she died, so that she wouldn't be aware of her pain and other symptoms. This is a legal practice, but there are no transparent guidelines on how it should be carried out; dying people and their families are often left confused as to what sedation is, if it is legal and if it is something they could have requested from the outset. Sedation provides a clear example of where power often resides in end-of-life decision-making.

Susan describes Fiona's final few days.

---

11 'The Inescapable Truth: How seventeen people a day will suffer as they die', Dignity in Dying, 2019.

It wasn't my decision. I would have hung onto her. The nurse said, 'I will ask you three times if that's what you want to do.' Fiona said, 'No, you know I've thought about it.' She wasn't able to move. She was finding it difficult to swallow, her tongue was swollen and she was finding it difficult to talk. The tumour was growing and she was getting clots at the back of her throat. It was just awful. She was in so much pain and no matter how much pain relief she was getting, it would just exacerbate it. It was always there.

They told us she wouldn't wake up; that she would slip away.

On the Friday the consultant came in and she said what did Fiona want to do? Did she want to make a decision before Monday? She said that she wanted it that day. She didn't want to wait for the weekend. We obviously thought that within hours Fiona would be asleep and that would be the end.

I stayed with her all night. She was still awake. We sat around the bed and put music on but she didn't sleep. She dozed on and off but she was awake more than she was asleep. You could have a conversation with her. She would say that she was thirsty or she wanted a drink.

She couldn't get comfortable, and she wanted me to keep moving the bed up and down because she couldn't move, but she just couldn't get comfortable. So that was the Friday. Saturday, she was still awake. Sunday, she was awake. Sunday, she was actually hungry. She wanted a milkshake and we went out to get her one. She had visitors.

Every day the dosage of ketamine was increasing. The consultant came in and said, 'Oh Fiona, I can't believe it. You're getting serious doses of drugs.'

On the Sunday there was a lovely nurse and she said, 'Shall we change the bed?' And I said, 'Yeah, I'll help you.' So we were changing Fiona's bed and she had fallen asleep for a bit. It was very frightening, because every time she did fall asleep, we kept thinking, 'That's it.' We had said goodbye, and you get upset, and then she'd suddenly wake up again, in a horrible way. This happened seven times. We were pleased to see her, but it was like being on a rollercoaster. It was very harrowing. Very harrowing. Your emotions are all over the place.

The nurses were also very, very upset. It was really

hard for them. I felt really sorry for them. One of the nurses would often be in tears, and she said, 'There's nothing else I can give her. I'm not allowed to give her any more. This is as much as I can give her. I can't take the pain away for her.'

On the Monday, they decided they were going to give her another syringe driver and move it from her arm to her leg. Then her breathing got shallower and shallower. The nurse came in to see her and said, 'Oh, her breathing is really shallow. I think her time's nearly out.' About fifteen minutes later she died.

It was very distressing for Fiona because she had to keep saying goodbye to everybody. We had to say good-bye to her, but she had to keep saying goodbye to all of us and that must have been awful for her. Absolutely dreadful. I wouldn't wish it on my worst enemy. To see somebody suffer... It was torture. Her illness was traumatic enough and how she coped with it was amazing.

I still feel quite traumatised by her death because I just think that it could have been avoided. I can't see the difference between giving somebody large amounts of drugs to end their suffering over a period of time or giving them all in one go. It just doesn't make sense, because the end result's the same. I just feel that at the end of the day she was let down.

I went to this meeting in London about palliative care. There was a professor at some university who said, 'What can we do to make people speak about dying? Because people don't broach the subject.' We were going around the room with people saying what their views were and people said, 'Oh yeah, I think that when I die I want to be in a middle of a field, in a bed, looking at the stars.' And I thought, that's not really reality. I said, 'Well, we broach it to a certain extent.' Then I brought up the subject of assisted dying, and I was shot down in flames and the professor swiftly moved on.

I feel like Fiona hasn't got a voice any more and I'm her voice. I'm the one who can tell her story and bring about change.

Most who read the report were shocked. Nick Boles, the former MP, wrote in the foreword that it was as harrowing as anything he had ever encountered as a Member of Parliament. Unsurprisingly, anger grew, much of it directed at Parliament's indifference to the fact that the current law condemned so many people to such horrific deaths.

What we hadn't expected was to be inundated with messages from bereaved relatives, who thanked us for validating their experiences. Many had previously questioned if they had imagined or over-dramatised their loved ones' suffering. Others had tried to be reassured by healthcare professionals that what they witnessed wasn't suffering but 'normal dying'. It was clear that we had stumbled upon a hidden and worrying problem.

Reacting on Twitter, a number of clinicians expressed their discomfort reading the report, not because of the misery contained within it but because they believed the accounts of bereaved relatives illustrated how people can misinterpret what happens to their loved ones as they die.

This questioning of people's perception of reality does not just appear to be aimed at bereaved relatives but at other doctors too. In the report, one palliative care consultant remembers a patient whose terminal cancer had spread to his penis, which had to be removed, leaving an open hole into his bladder:

He was a very gentle person. He was so ashamed and he would cry. He was begging to have his life ended because he just hated it and he had lived for months in that condition. He was begging to have his life ended because it had absolutely no meaning. He was also in pain, but that was not the main thing; it was the utter degradation. I felt so helpless. We could do nothing about that.

Other recollections included in the report were equally disturbing: a father becoming a skeleton while he actively starved himself to death; a mother vomiting black bile uncontrollably; a man caring for his sister on her deathbed as faecal matter came out of her mouth; women expressing the deep psychological suffering that stems from fungating wounds, which can happen when breast cancer breaks through the skin. Why try to deny these people their truth?

Gaslighting is a psychological phenomenon where one person causes another to question their perception of reality, often through subtle manipulation of their environment and questioning of what they previously accepted as fact. Gaslighting is often a feature of abusive relationships, as its destabilising effects induce an emotional dependence on the abuser. The practice of medical gaslighting – which manifests itself in various ways, but ultimately involves a doctor, perhaps unintentionally, persuading someone to think they are exaggerating the severity of their condition or symptoms – is not unknown.

Women are particularly likely to be on the receiving end of this form of gaslighting. Whether implicit or premeditated, it is not only unethical but causes tangible harm. Research suggests that despite being more likely to experience chronic pain women are less likely than men to have their pain managed in line with clinical guidelines.[12] One study showed that women were half as likely as men to be prescribed painkillers following coronary bypass surgery.[13] This affects other groups too; black and Hispanic women report receiving less pain relief than white women following childbirth.[14]

---

12 'Sex differences in chronic pain management practices for patients receiving opioids from the Veterans Health Administration', *Pain Medicine* (2015), vol. 16, no. 1, pp. 112–18.

13 'The influence of gender on the frequency of pain and sedative medication administered to postoperative patients', *Sex Roles* (1990), vol. 23, nos 11–12, pp. 713–25.

14 'Racial disparities in postpartum pain management', *Obstetrics & Gynecology* (2019), vol. 134, no. 6, pp. 1147–53.

Gaslighting can take more subtle forms. The organisation Birthrights works to improve people's experience of pregnancy and childbirth. They say they see too many cases of women being given falsely reassuring information about childbirth, which can cause distress further down the line. They also know of women who have been belittled, dismissed and bullied because of the choices they want to make about their own pregnancies.[15]

This cannot happen around death and dying. We need to be honest about the fact that some people will die in pain. The figure of 'seventeen a day' taken from the title of our report is the number of people who would die in severe pain every day even if everybody had access to the very best palliative care. The figure was calculated by the Office of Health Economics (OHE), who described it as the most conservative estimate they could make based on current research.

We do nothing to dissipate fear of death and dying if we are not honest about it – or, worse, if we actively suppress the truth. To keep aspects of dying shrouded in secrecy

---

15 'Why we need to have more honest conversations with women about how birth might unfold…', Birthrights, 2019.

is to negate genuine fear; to tell everyone it will be OK is to invalidate the experiences of real people for whom it was not OK, and the experiences of their loved ones who bore witness to their pain. There is no need to tolerate suffering as collateral damage. We have to accept the reality that dying can be scary. We then have to accept that it is reasonable for people to want an option to escape a period of unnecessary suffering, should that be their wish.

The voice of dying people

In Marcel Proust's classic novel *In Search of Lost Time*, the narrator observes:

> The thoughts of the dying are quite often turned towards the aspect of death that is real, painful, dark, visceral, towards the underside of death, which is in fact the side it presents to them and so harshly makes them feel, and which more closely resembles a crushing burden, a difficulty breathing, a need to drink, than what we call the idea of death.[16]

---

16 Marcel Proust, *In Search of Lost Time, Volume 1: The Way by Swann's* (London: Penguin Classics, 2003).

History has been consumed by the 'idea' of death, often at the expense of the people who are facing the reality of it. Professor David Clark, biographer of Cicely Saunders, and a leading academic in end-of-life care, has written that in Victorian times, a prolonged death – what we might now think of as a bad death – was viewed by many as a spiritual test and an opportunity for a dying person to rekindle or establish a relationship with Christ.[17]

In our more secular world, we now need to find a new way of considering dying that acknowledges and deals with the aspects of death that are at the forefront of the minds of people coming to the ends of their lives. To do that, we must listen carefully not to religious scripture, philosophers or medical rulebooks of the past, but to dying people themselves.

Noel Conway was diagnosed with motor neurone disease (MND) in 2014. Noel is a fearless campaigner whose two-year legal battle to change the law, while not

---

17 David Clark, *To Comfort Always: A history of palliative medicine since the nineteenth century* (Oxford: Oxford University Press, 2016).

succeeding in itself, undoubtedly added another weight to the scale that will one day tip in favour of reform.

Noel once spoke to a colleague of ours about his frustrations at how patients, and those caring for them, have been characterised as 'happy warriors and angels'. While this stereotyping is palatable for some, it doesn't leave space for others to confront the dark side of terminal illness or to acknowledge the cruelties of a disease like MND and its inevitable progression. This is part of a larger lexicon of 'battle language', which gives rise to the pernicious idea that those who die have not fought hard enough. This narrative allows patients to talk about living with and trying to overcome a disease, however implausible that may be, but not about the realities of dying with it. Accepting death, and articulating a wish for the choice of an assisted death, can seem to some as a sign of defeat. Yet imprisoning dying people in a cage of relentless positivity illustrates nothing more than denial. Why can't we accept that some people would find more value in a hastened but peaceful death than they would in continuing to struggle to extend life for the sake of it? Noel loves life and does not want it to end. He didn't ask to be diagnosed with MND, but he is not prepared to shy away from the fact that one day he will want control over how and when he dies.

Noel suggested that, rather than being constructed to respond to the needs of dying people, the unwritten rules governing how people talk about the end of life ignore the messy parts of dying. Noel has been open about how he has confronted these himself.

Imagine you have motor neurone disease – an incurable, terminal disease that will kill you, but not before it causes progressive deterioration of the muscles throughout your body. You have three choices about how to die.

The first one involves removing a breathing aid, which is used for 22 hours a day, and will result in breathlessness and suffocation that can only be relieved by medication.

Unfortunately, the medication will cause a state of drowsy semi-consciousness until death occurs.

This experience may last for a few hours or a few days; no one knows and no one can say how much that will alleviate the sensation of fighting for breath.

The second choice is to wait until the breathing aid

is used all the time, so that, when removed, death will come more swiftly.

However, the drawback here is that the body will by then have become virtually immobile.

What must it be like to lie there unable to move one's head from side to side, to be able to move only one's eyes?

I have some premonition of that now, when I don't even have the strength to get my arms and hands from beneath the sheet and single blanket which I use at night. It takes a great deal of self-control not to panic.

Finally, there is the choice, if the law is changed, to permit assisted dying in this country.[18]

With our current approach to death and dying, there is little room to deviate from the notion that everything will be OK, even if the dying person themselves has arrived at the conclusion that everything is not in fact OK. They are dying, and that can be scary because they may be forced to suffer against their wishes.

18 'I can't move and can hardly breathe: Let me die with dignity', Sky News, 1 May 2018.

These are harsh truths but ones we can't ignore. If the culture around death and dying is misaligned with dying people then perhaps it needs a jolt to get it back on track.

Perhaps doctors do not wish to 'burden' their patients with the truth, or are unwilling to burden themselves with the fears of their patients, fears that would be more likely to occur if a person knows what may lie ahead for them. Or perhaps it is an indication that the 'doctor knows best' approach still exists. Two doctors, arguing against assisted dying, wrote in the *BMJ* in early 2020 that a dying person 'may already feel redundant when he or she, racked with despair, makes a *rational* request for assisted dying'.[19] Questioning the validity of a person's decisions based on a value judgement of their circumstances is paternalism in action. No life is easy and each of us is moulded by the adversity we have had to overcome or endure throughout our lives. The way we navigate a course through life is in many ways determined by our spectacular ability to make

---

19 'Assisted dying—a form of abandonment?', *BMJ Opinion*, 7 February 2020.

decisions even in the most difficult of circumstances. It is therefore deeply patronising to suggest that those who are diagnosed with a terminal illness suddenly become irretrievably vulnerable, and incapable of utilising mechanisms of choice and control precisely at the time when those things become most valuable.

Dismissing people's wishes because we think we understand the conditions that have given rise to them better than they do themselves should be anathema. Of course, society must offer support and qualified professionals should explore motivations – perhaps unconscious ones – carefully, *with* dying people. But we have to move away from the assumption that people do not know what is best for themselves. Men dictating to women. Straight people dictating to gay people. White people dictating to people of colour. People who are not dying dictating to people who are dying. We have to respect each person's lived experience.

The actor Lord Brian Rix was a prominent disability rights campaigner and president of Mencap. In 2006, he voted against a proposed assisted dying law but in 2016 he reversed his stance:

As a dying man, who has been dying now for several weeks, I am only too conscious that the laws of this country make it impossible for people like me to be helped on their way [...] I think it's wrong that people like me are stranded like this. I'm not looking for something that helps me only, I'm thinking of all the other people who must be in the same dreadful position.[20]

Lord Rix died just days after writing this letter. Those who do not move do not feel their chains. It was only in his final weeks, as the lack of control over his fate became apparent, that Lord Rix began to feel the chains around his limbs.

The dying people we have had the pleasure of meeting and working with are the strongest people we have ever met. It has been incredible to witness their resilience while their pleas for legalised assisted dying have been shouted over and ignored. Like all true heroes, each defeat makes them bolder, and we are in awe of those who have chosen to speak out and stand on the

---

20 'Terminally ill actor Brian Rix calls for assisted dying law change', BBC News, 8 August 2016.

shoulders of the giants that have gone before them. Here is a group of dying people perfectly capable of talking about death, and as a society we are not listening to what they have to say.

At a hospice sector conference in 2017, a palliative care doctor referred to those who seek an assisted death in Switzerland as 'control-freaks', a distasteful attempt to 'other' those who want to exercise the most natural instinct: self-determination. There is nothing freak-ish about wanting a degree of control that allows you to avoid suffering and die on your own terms. Again, we must be attuned to the possibility of some doctors abusing their power and dismissing the wishes of dying people because of their own prejudices.

We would urge organisations that work with dying people to be brave. You might feel that this issue is too treacherous to engage with; and yes, there are those who passionately oppose assisted dying, often because of deeply held moral and religious beliefs, but that is not a reason to appease those people or ignore the flaws in the status quo they promote.

This is a zero-sum game. Inaction isn't a passive

choice; it condemns thousands more to a horrible death. Please listen to what dying people are saying. People who are dying want, need and deserve the option of a safeguarded assisted dying law. They are calling out for it; Dignity in Dying should not be the only one trying to draw attention to their voices.

We often wonder how quickly the law would change if dead people could talk. The tragedy of our cause is that the people our law impacts the most have no means through which to share their first-hand accounts of how they died. Contrast this with the #MeToo movement. When people spoke out together, it lit a fire that burned through widespread abuse, assault and misogyny. There can be no hiding when survivors speak their truth. Perhaps we are guilty of neglecting what we force the dead to endure because they are silent?

It is more important than ever that we consider these issues. The coronavirus pandemic has exposed aspects of dying that we have been failing to get right, failings that are too easy to ignore under normal circumstances but which now awkwardly puncture our perception of reality, like a rare low tide reveals forgotten shipwrecks.

In response to the pandemic, some GPs and healthcare providers issued blanket Do Not Attempt Cardio-Pulmonary Resuscitation orders (DNACPRs), particularly to older people or those with underlying health conditions. As the reaction from the relevant authorities soon made clear, issuing blanket orders and communicating these decisions via a generic letter – or, in some cases, not communicating them at all – demonstrated little regard for people's feelings, for national guidance or indeed, in many cases, for the law. This was a dismal but faultless illustration of our dysfunctional relationship with dying: a valuable nugget of good intent buried somewhere in a heap of perplexing poor practice.

For most people with a terminal condition, their heart stopping is a signal that their life has come to an end. This is rarely an event which can be reversed. When someone is dying, there is very little chance that CPR will prevent death, and it is a brutally violent act. If a person is subjected to inappropriate CPR, they will likely die with broken ribs, with a tube inserted into their throat, and alone, their frightened family members having been ushered out of the room moments earlier. Even if it is successful, for most people with an underlying condition it will only defer death by days – days marred by the presence of broken bones, potential brain damage caused by oxygen deprivation and the shadow of unnecessary trauma. While DNACPRs offer the protection of ensuring inappropriate CPR does not take place, they do not prevent other care being provided. They do not deny people pain relief, comfort care or even other forms of life-saving treatments such as antibiotics, unless further conversations about those decisions have been had.

DNACPRs are important tools – without them, we would see more people dying in unnecessarily distressing circumstances – however, there is a frequent problem in how they are communicated to ensure people do not feel disempowered or abandoned. The fact that some doctors felt it was acceptable to communicate DNACPRs in such an insensitive way at a time of crisis highlights how badly we have got things wrong. Why hadn't these discussions already taken place? If a GP deemed it inappropriate for one of their patients to be subjected to CPR then they should have already had that conversation with them. It shouldn't have taken a national emergency to prompt the decision. Again, it is the culture around medicine, rather than individual doctors, who are to blame. And it comes back to honesty. If people who were already dying or frail or had underlying conditions understood the consequences of CPR, they would be less likely to expect it; a preference not to receive it could then have been discussed and documented, and there would not have been a sudden panic to issue blanket orders at the outset of the pandemic. Yet if we are not honest and frank around other aspects of dying, why should we expect this around CPR? Doesn't withholding the truth about the grim realities of dying encourage a culture where people do not have to make these decisions for themselves? The fact that doctors are much more likely than their patients to refuse aggressive interventions such as CPR suggests the route out of this problem is to bridge the knowledge gap.[21] Yet sadly, even with our newfound willingness to confront our mortality, there is reluctance from some to open up

---

21 'Are doctors more likely to refuse CPR?', *The Atlantic*, 26 July 2012.

this level of conversation. For example, when columnist and patient advocate Dr Phil Hammond asked on Twitter for more detail on whether a death from coronavirus would be unpleasant or peaceful, he was told by many of his colleagues that it was inappropriate to ask the question in a public forum.[22]

Without a new culture of honesty around dying, DNACPRs will always be symbolic of the power imbalance that exists at the end of life. They are ultimately a communication tool for clinicians, so regardless of their necessity, and even if they are accompanied by honest, sensitive discussions, the individual can only ever be a passenger in the process. They are of course an important tool in protecting an individual from a potentially futile and invasive treatment, but for those who can make their own decisions, a DNACPR order should ideally come at the end point of a process of planning led by the dying person themselves. We believe it is recognition of this power imbalance, even if the recognition is innate and unarticulated, that gives rise to

22 @drphilhammond, 16 April 2020, https://twitter.com/drphilhammond/status/1250832059632947200.

public mistrust around DNACPRs and the subsequent frustration that clinicians feel when their well-meaning efforts to reduce suffering are misinterpreted as something more sinister.

Some compared GPs who had responded to coronavirus by contacting people to tell them CPR would not be in their best interests to Josef Mengele, the 'Angel of Death', who disguised his monstrous experiments and murders of prisoners in Nazi concentration camps as medical inquisitiveness. This analogy was rightly condemned as 'abhorrent and distasteful'.[23] The way DNACPRs were applied en masse was at best insensitive and at worst illegal, but surely nobody really believes GPs were using the pandemic to smuggle eugenics into mainstream medical practice? It is understandable why doctors felt affronted by this suggestion, yet it also reminds us that doctors themselves have often been guilty of sinking to such depths. In 2012, the president of the Royal College of GPs cited Mengele's crimes when she questioned why assisted dying commanded

---

23 'The truth about do not resuscitate orders', *The Independent*, 9 April 2020.

such great support from the public.[24] Perhaps this is a lesson that resorting to disparaging, hyperbolic comparisons does nothing to further healthy, rational debate or to promote shared understanding between people with different perspectives.

While efforts to educate the public around the role of DNACPRs are important, because this will always be a clinician-led process, we suspect it might be a near-impossible task unless accompanied by a radical rethink of how we approach death and dying – one that doesn't just address the indefensible outright ban on assisted dying but also incorporates other means of empowerment that will allow dying people to be the masters of their own fate.

Dignity in Dying's sister charity Compassion in Dying supports thousands of people every year to think about, document and communicate their preferences for the treatment and care they will receive at the end of life. In England and Wales, there are legal tools such as living wills (Advance Decisions), Advance

---

24 Iona Heath, 'What's wrong with assisted dying', *BMJ* (2012), doi: https://doi.org/10.1136/bmj.e3755.

Statements and Lasting Powers of Attorney that are unacceptably under-utilised. In Scotland and Northern Ireland, similar tools are available. These measures enable people to set out their wishes in advance or appoint someone they trust to make decisions on their behalf if they lose the capacity to do so themselves. Psychologically, knowing that these tools are in place – and, unlike DNACPRs, these are tools that individuals can instigate and complete themselves – to ensure they do not receive treatment they do not want can bring people the same levels of comfort and reassurance as having the option of an assisted death.

Compassion in Dying has spoken to many people throughout the pandemic who do not want to be admitted to hospital if they start to experience symptoms of coronavirus. They don't want treatment to prolong their life, they especially don't want to be treated in an intensive care unit with mechanical ventilation, treatment which is invasive and far from guaranteed to succeed. Some people we speak to do want all treatment that is available to them, while others want some treatments but not others, but many want to be in control of their deaths and have made the choice that they would rather refuse treatment and die at home than risk dying alone on a hospital ward. Some of these people have already documented their wish to refuse treatment in different circumstances, such as if they have dementia or a brain injury. Others are considering their future care for the first time. Some people are older, frail, with multiple health conditions. Others are healthy and simply want to ensure their wishes are known should something happen to them in the future.

We support people to record their wishes and we explain how best they should be communicated with clinicians so that they are respected. These forms of planning are invaluable. By chipping away at the uncertainty that surrounds dying, people gain peace of mind. They report feeling empowered. They have exercised control over some of the things that will happen as they die. And having thought through and documented their wishes lessens the burden on a clinician who may have otherwise needed to guess, in a moment of crisis, the treatment a person might have wanted or not wanted to receive. As author Diana Melly puts it, 'Facing death and dying head on and planning for it is essential to give us all the best chance of a good death. It is not brave; it is the right and sensible thing to do.'[25] While there are efforts afoot at a national level to embed advance care planning into the NHS, the fact that we have not yet found a way to implement a culture of planning for the end of our lives into day-to-day medical practice is a great failure of our age.

Being able to plan for our deaths and having the option of controlling the manner and timing of our deaths are not distinct concepts; they both serve to achieve the aim of ensuring that people, as much as is possible, have the death they want to have. So why does our law draw a distinction? It is inconsistent to say that people's preferences at the end of life are paramount and then flagrantly disregard the public's demand for the option of assisted dying. A relatively recent evolution in policy now encourages clinicians to reframe conversations from 'What's wrong with you?' to 'What matters to you?'. This is a step in the right direction, but

---

25 'It's not brave to plan for dying – it helps me to carry on living', HuffPost, 15 April 2020.

it is of little value if we don't listen to the answer. We know meaningful choice and control matter to dying people, so why haven't we given it to them? We can't pick and choose which wishes of dying people are valid and which aren't.

It seems that whichever aspects of end-of-life care we shine a light on we uncover a similar pattern of problems. Practice is struggling to adapt to the demands of modern society, and while the patient voice gets louder this only serves to highlight how deeply we have buried it. We are in thrall to an archaic culture within medicine which, inadvertently or not, disempowers the individual. It is our reliance on that flawed culture which props up a law that denies people meaningful choice over how their lives end.

The consequences of this relationship between medical practice and the legislation governing how we die are dire.

Part II

Hard truths

THE PHRASE 'HARD cases make bad law' is often repeated by those who resent the fact that dying people and their families are speaking out about the injustices they face. Even if the cases mentioned in this book were very rare examples, this would be a deeply insensitive response to people's suffering.

Yet we know that the 'hard cases' that make the news are just the tip of the iceberg, with thousands more happening every year that we as a society have tacitly decided to disregard. A more reasonable conclusion would be that 'bad laws make hard cases'.

As we saw above, we are often told that dying is not as bad as we think, but anyone who has read our 'Inescapable Truth' report will realise that dying can be far worse than we might ever have imagined. Our unwillingness to accommodate this truth into our law has given rise to makeshift alternatives, an unpleasant menu of choices that people can use to take matters into their own hands.

These were the options that Dennis Eccleston faced when he was looking for a way out of his suffering. Others have faced these options too and been forced into similarly tragic decisions.

None of these options are acceptable replacements for a safeguarded, transparent, assisted dying law and they all pose difficult questions for those who persist in defending our status quo.

A one-way trip to Switzerland

Dear Members of Parliament,

By the time you read this, I will be dead.

On Thursday 7th February 2019, I will have taken medication that will end my life, surrounded by my wife, Ann, my children, Alix and Dominic, and a couple of my dearest friends at the Dignitas facility in Switzerland. With their love and support I have been able to fulfil my final wish: to be in control of my end, rather than endure the immense suffering motor neurone disease had in store for me.

I want to impress upon you the anguish me and my family have experienced, not because of this awful illness (though of course this has been incredibly difficult), but because of the law against assisted dying in this country. The blanket ban on assisted dying has not only forced me to spend thousands of pounds and endure months of logistical hurdles in order to secure a peaceful and dignified death overseas but it has meant that my final weeks of life have been blighted by visits from social services and police.

Since my diagnosis of MND, an incurable, terminal illness, in 2016, I felt as though bombs have been dropping on me. I gradually lost the use of all four limbs. My ability to speak, swallow and breathe began rapidly deteriorating. I knew my death was inevitable and unavoidable, but I remained strong for my family. I am 80 years old and have lived a full life. I did not fear death, but I did fear the journey. I simply wanted to cut this suffering short by a few months. When I eventually got the 'green light' from Dignitas, a weight lifted; I was able to get on with living without the constant mental anguish over my death.

But then, as I was saying my final goodbyes and preparing myself for the end, the final, biggest bomb dropped and I could no longer keep it together. This bomb was in fact an anonymous phone call to social services who informed the police of my plans to go to Switzerland. Within hours Ann and I were facing a criminal investigation. The thought that I might not make it to Switzerland, or that, if I did, Ann might be facing 14 years in jail for helping me, was almost too much to bear.

In 52 years of marriage, Ann had not seen me cry. The day we were contacted by the police, I sobbed.

The law in this country robbed me of control over my death. It forced me to seek solace in Switzerland. Then it sought to punish those attempting to help me get there. The hypocrisy and cruelty of this is astounding. Though it is perfectly legal for me to make arrangements and travel to Dignitas by myself, the minute anyone else 'assists' me in any way – which is essential, due to my condition – they are liable for prosecution.

I had the chance, just over a week before my death, to

speak to some MPs and Peers about my experience and my adamant wish that the law should be changed. The overwhelming reaction in the room was one of agreement; however, I am aware that despite huge public support for an assisted dying law, most members of parliament currently oppose it. I spoke to one MP who had voted against the last assisted dying Bill in 2015. The law being proposed was limited to terminally ill, mentally competent adults in their final months, with strict inbuilt safeguards to protect the vulnerable and anyone else who has not made a clear decision of their own volition. When I pressed her on why she felt people like me should be denied a say over our own death and be forced to suffer, she was unable to articulate an answer.

I want MPs to know that change is urgently needed and that it is achievable – over 100 million people in several American and Australian states and across Canada are covered by assisted dying laws which allow choice to dying people and protection to others. No family should ever have to endure the torment we have undergone in recent weeks, but it will be easier to bear knowing that by sharing it we can contribute to future change. I sincerely hope that you will truly listen to our story and see the suffering you are inflicting by upholding the status quo.

Yours sincerely,

Geoffrey Whaley

Chalfont St Peter, Buckinghamshire

7 February 2019

*   *   *

Since it opened in 1998, 3,027 people around the world have arranged an assisted death with Dignitas, 457 of them from Britain. Data from Dignitas shows that its popularity, for want of a better word, has increased over time. Twice as many Britons used Dignitas between 2010 and 2019 as did so between 2000 and 2009. Membership has nearly doubled in the past five years. Three other similar facilities have opened to meet the growing demand.[26]

So accepted is the fact that someone can, technically, have an assisted death if they want one by travelling to

---

26 'Statistics', Dignitas (2020).

Switzerland that some people feel this is reason in itself not to change the law in the UK. There are obvious flaws in this logic. Claiming that assisted dying is wrong and should be avoided no matter the consequences while also accepting the reality that people can already access assisted dying elsewhere is a weak position to take, the cruelty of which deepens with the more understanding one has of just how difficult having an assisted death in Switzerland can be.

One difficulty that the coronavirus pandemic has shed light on is the harm caused by people not being able to hold funerals for their loved ones, with fears that this may lead to more acute grief and long-term detrimental effects on people's mental health. To avoid triggering a criminal investigation, facilities that provide assisted dying in Switzerland recommend cremations, with ashes being made available to families at a later date. Many bereaved relatives have described to us the great pain that results from not being able to hold a funeral for their loved one who has died in Switzerland, a stark reminder of the sacrifices people currently have to make to die on their terms.

Assisted dying is legal in Switzerland because the Swiss penal code only criminalises assisting someone to end their own life if the motives are selfish. In other words, compassionate assistance is not treated as a crime. Because (unlike elsewhere in the world) there is no specific piece of legislation setting out eligibility criteria, there is no residency requirement, so there is nothing stopping facilities providing assisted dying to foreign nationals. Switzerland is unique in this sense.

As Geoff's letter sets out in painful clarity, the current law makes a criminal of anyone who helps somebody to arrange an assisted death overseas. In 2009, following Debbie Purdy's successful case, which Dignity in Dying initiated and supported, the then Director of Public Prosecutions (DPP) Sir Keir Starmer published his policy outlining the circumstances that would be more or less likely to give rise to a prosecution for assisting a suicide. The policy sets out sixteen factors and, taken collectively, these suggest that if assistance has been provided compassionately and the person who has died was an adult acting voluntarily then a prosecution will be less likely. However, the policy provides no guarantees and still requires all suspected cases to be investigated by police. As *The Times* agreed when the ruling was made, this was a victory for common sense and compassion, but one that only stressed the need for more fundamental revision of the law.[27]

Since the DPP's policy was published, 156 cases of assisting suicide have been referred to the Crown Prosecution Service (CPS) by police. Of these 156 cases, the CPS did not proceed with 105, and thirty-one cases were withdrawn by the police. Just three cases have been successfully prosecuted.[28]

Some say that this is evidence of the law working well. Crimes are investigated, yet relatives who help their loved one get to Dignitas are unlikely to feel the full force of the law. Such an observation is often accompanied by the mawkish maxim 'the law has a stern face but a kind heart'. We would question whether Ann Whaley's investigation by police, the one that brought her husband Geoff to tears of fear and anxiety, is evidence of the law's kind heart, but perhaps the people who put forward this argument have no experience or understanding of what it feels like to be accused of breaking the law.

---

27 'Life and death', *The Times*, 31 July 2009.

28 'Latest assisted suicide figures', Crown Prosecution Service (2020), updated as of January 2020.

Yet this assertion contains a more elementary error in logic. All cases of assisting a suicide should be investigated by police, yet we know, from the figures released by Dignitas and others, that most are not. Hundreds of deaths have simply gone under the radar of police. We would ask those who think that the current law is safe what protections they believe are in place for the assisted deaths our society already tacitly accepts. And even if every case was investigated, are we really in a position to call that 'safe', given that safeguards only kick in after the person has died? Our law is failing to deter, punish or reform effectively. On what grounds does it work?

We are not suggesting for a second that the police should step up their efforts in investigating these cases. We have spoken to bereaved relatives who sit in both camps: those who've had that frightening knock on the door from the police while they're still nervously waiting to be reunited with their loved one's remains (usually it is a neighbour or a friend of a friend who notifies the authorities); and also those who have returned to the UK and have been left alone, but who walk the streets suspicious of any police officer they see, not knowing if they are at risk of investigation. We are told that the anxiety lessens with time but does not ever go away.

In 2019, half of the Police and Crime Commissioners in England and Wales wrote to the Secretary of State for Justice to advocate for a review of the current law. They said that the law 'has caused distress, confusion and pain for dying people, their loved ones, and even the investigating police officers themselves', adding that 'the cost of these investigations – financial, emotional and societal – cannot be easily dismissed'.[29] If those tasked with enforcing the law recognise that it is broken, is it not time we re-examined it?

Debbie Purdy's victory was hard-won and her legacy is cemented, though the shortcomings of the DPP's policy were put beyond doubt during the debate on the Assisted Dying Bill in 2015, when Sir Keir Starmer, by then an MP, recognised the limits of the policy he had authored:

> We have arrived at a position where compassionate, ama-
> teur assistance from nearest and dearest is accepted but
> professional medical assistance is not, unless someone

---

29 'Assisted dying law does not work', *Law Society Gazette*, 30 October 2019.

has the means and physical assistance to get to Dignitas. That to my mind is an injustice that we have trapped
within our current arrangement.[30]

The other injustice we have created is a financial one,
leading to a discriminatory two-tier system of dying.
The average cost of an assisted death in Switzerland is
around £10,000. Sixty-six per cent of people would be
willing to break the law to help a loved one die in Switzerland if that were their wish, yet only 25 per cent of
people would be able to afford it.[31] The vast majority of
people are being denied a peaceful death simply because
of their socio-economic status.

In 2015, two sisters tried to raise money to enable
their mother, who had motor neurone disease, to have
the death she wanted in Switzerland. The group Care
Not Killing reported them to the police, who advised
the daughters to stop trying to raise funds because it
would leave them susceptible to prosecution. Ultimately,
Dignitas offered the woman in question a reduced fee

---

30 Hansard, HC Deb, 11 September 2015, vol. 599, col. 674.
31 YouGov, 2017.

after an anonymous donation was made to them. Her daughters, still fearing interference from the police, told reporters that they 'would stay out of Britain for a while' in order to have space to grieve.[32]

Even if somebody has a spare £10,000 and has people around them who are not deterred by the threat of criminal prosecution, an assisted death in Switzerland may not be possible. Terminal illnesses often lead to a rapid decline in a person's physical capabilities. For many dying people, a short trip to the hospital needs planning and time. Even without travel restrictions, it is simply not an option for some people to get a taxi to an airport, board a commercial plane, arrive in a unfamiliar (and expensive) foreign country, check into a hotel, have an appointment with a doctor, then get another taxi the next day to the facility where the assisted death will take place. For many of those who are desperate to control the manner and timing of their death, this journey is simply impossible.

As a result, many people end their lives much sooner

---

32 'A last family photo with her two daughters by her side... then terminally-ill mother dies in bed at Dignitas clinic in Switzerland', MailOnline, 9 November 2015.

than they might otherwise choose to. It means that people are forced into an unenviable decision of finding the moment that strikes the right balance of maximising time at home with their loved ones without risking their last bit of freedom slipping away from them.

Once a decision is made, it's not possible to just book the next flight and turn up at Dignitas's door. This is a procedure that needs weeks if not months of organising. There are legal obligations that organisations in Switzerland must meet. This means they need paperwork: birth certificates, marriage certificates, dental records, medical reports. These can be difficult to obtain and doctors are understandably cautious about doing anything that looks as though they might be encouraging or helping an assisted death in any way. Current guidance provided to doctors about what they can and can't do to help someone lacks clarity. Many people fall at this hurdle. For those who do manage to gather these documents, it adds to the significant emotional turmoil, as one of our supporters has told us:

> I'd said to my Mum, 'Look, whatever happens, whatever you need, I'll help you do it. I'll help you do this.' I had

taken responsibility. It was awful, because I just wanted to cry. I just wanted to spend time with my Mum, and I wanted to be able to cherish those moments. But I was sitting there writing letters or doing paperwork. Just constantly … I lost my job, because they couldn't take me being out of the workplace while I was going through this process.[33]

It is testament to the strength of the love that binds families and friends together that people are willing to make these sacrifices to enable someone they care about to have the death they want for themselves.

We can also learn a lot about dying people's yearning for the option of an assisted death by the fact that so many put themselves through this arduous journey, because of the immense value they place on the comfort that is offered at its final destination. These people know that they will die away from their homes; they will hopefully be surrounded by loved ones, but perhaps not as many as they may have wished for, knowing that the greater the number of attendees, the more accessories to

---

33 'The True Cost: How the UK outsources death to Dignitas', Dignity in Dying, 2017.

the crime there are. Yet this is all preferable to leaving the manner of their death in the hands of fate.

As Elaine Selly, who accompanied her husband Richard to Dignitas in 2019, said, 'We wished we weren't there and we didn't have to go through this.'[34]

DIY

In Victoria, Australia, coroners submitted evidence to parliamentarians which outlined the appalling lengths dying people would go to in order to exercise control over their deaths. It was so shocking that it forced many to question how they could continue defending the law as it then stood. Assisted dying is now legal in Victoria, and Western Australia soon followed Victoria's lead.

A suicide researcher in New Zealand changed his mind on assisted dying having encountered too much evidence of terminally ill people being left with no other option but to end their own life in extreme circumstances. He writes: 'In the course of my research I was struck by the

---

34 'Richard Selley: Wife's "awful" journey to husband's assisted death', BBC News, 12 October 2019.

violence and indignity of the methods that were used to effect self-euthanasia (for instance, taping a bag over one's head, and handcuffing oneself having swallowed the key) as well as the negative effects on loved ones.'[35]

In Connecticut, Kevin Conners was charged with manslaughter in 2019 for helping his wife end her own life. Lori Conners had ovarian cancer which had spread throughout her body and was causing constant pain. Kevin held the gun to her head because she didn't think she would be able to hold it steady. She pulled the trigger.[36]

In 2018, Michael Parkins was told he had just weeks to live due to heart failure. He wanted to be referred to Dignitas, though his doctors told him bluntly that they were unable to do this. Instead, he threw himself from a multi-storey carpark, which resulted in 'multiple and catastrophic injuries' from which he died. The coroner concluded that Mr Parkins's wishes for how he wanted to die were 'unfulfillable', which is what led him to take

---

35 Affidavit of John Charles Weaver, Seales v Attorney-General [2015] NZHC 1239.
36 'Man faces manslaughter charge for helping cancer-stricken wife die by suicide', *USA Today*, 14 December 2019.

such drastic action. A psychiatrist who had assessed Mr Parkins prior to his death had said that he had clear 'logic and coherence' in his reasoning for wanting to die on his own terms and that depression or other mental illness had been ruled out.[37] In places where assisted dying is legal, similar psychiatric assessments are carried out for anybody whose capacity is in doubt.

For the past five years, the indefatigable campaigner Dr Jacky Davis has led the charge in highlighting why it is unsustainable for the medical establishment to persist with its long-standing opposition to law change. Jacky's brother had terminal cancer and, after making sure he was alone in the house so that his loved ones would not be held accountable for his death, he tried to hang himself. His attempt failed. He was eventually found dead in a pool of blood at the bottom of a flight of stairs. Nobody knows what he went through in those final hours of his life.[38]

---

37 'Call for change in the law after man's tragic death in Plymouth city centre', *Plymouth Herald*, 20 February 2018.

38 'Doctor calls for a change in assisted suicide law after her dying brother took his own life', *Daily Mirror*, 20 June 2015.

As campaigners, we know of countless other stories. One that haunts us is of a man dying of motor neurone disease who was clear he wanted to end his life on his terms. He spoke to his wife about this. He recorded a video to say that what he was about to do was his own choice and that he hadn't been encouraged or assisted. He had ruled out being able to hang himself, though he thought he could inflict a wound that would lead to his death. He said his goodbyes to his wife, who then went for lunch with her friend, without being able to tell the friend why she had left her husband alone. Her husband went into the woods on his motorised wheelchair, but he didn't have the strength to do what he wanted to do. His wife said, 'He'd left it too long. So, he came back on his mobility scooter and then I came back and you can imagine … He was absolutely distraught with himself, a) because he hadn't managed it and b) because I was also distraught.'

Simon Sandberg, who accompanied his friend Simon Binner to Life Circle (an organisation which, like Dignitas, provides assistance to non-residents of Switzerland), said that it was only when Simon, who had motor neurone disease, tried to hang himself on his grandchildren's swing and then attempted to throw himself out of his bedroom window that those around him realised how desperate he was not to see out the final weeks of his disease.

In a 2019 House of Commons debate to examine the failures of our current law, prompted by Geoff Whaley's death, Paul Blomfield MP shared his story.

> It is, by a coincidence, the eighth anniversary to the day of my receiving a phone call here in Westminster that my father had been found dead in his garage. The previous night, he had tidied up his belongings, left small piles of money to settle the bills with the newsagent and others, and written final notes. He had then walked to the garage, connected a hosepipe from his car exhaust into the car, taken an overdose and switched on the engine. As hon. Members can see, I do not find this easy to talk about, even after eight years, but I have done so before and I will do so today, not least because I know that he would have wanted me to, as somebody who had always believed in a change in the law on assisted dying.
>
> My father was eighty-seven. At that age, he had inevitably watched many of his friends go, often miserably. He

talked in particular of one friend who had become con-
fined to bed, doubly incontinent, and – having become
both deaf and blind – unable to communicate with anybody. My father saw no point in that kind of life and had
always said that he would rather end things than face a
degrading death. He was somebody who had made the
most of his life: he had a tough East End upbringing
in poverty, became an RAF pilot in the war and built
a successful business career. He had his share of health
problems but faced them all positively. He was not afraid
of pain, but he could not face the indignity of a lingering
death, and I am sure that he made up his mind to take his
life soon after receiving a terminal diagnosis of inoper-
able lung cancer. But he still died prematurely, and I am
sure that what drove him to end his life at that point was
the fear that if he did not act when he could and was still
able to do so, he would lose the opportunity to act at all.
He could not talk to me or his partner about it, because
he would have made us complicit. The current law forced
my father into a lonely decision and a lonely death.

Some people will say that we simply need to improve
end-of-life care, and it is hugely important that we do.

My father supported our local hospice and I raise funds for it. It does a great job, but no hospice can enable everybody to die with the dignity that they would want. Indeed, for my father, it was soon after his appointment with a palliative care nurse where together they talked about his last months that he took the decision to take his life. If the law had made it possible, he could have shared his plans with us, and knowing that he could, with support, go at the time of his choosing would have enabled him to stay longer. If the law had made it possible, he would have been able to say goodbye and go with his family around him, not in a carbon monoxide-filled garage. He, and many others like him, deserve better. We simply need to change the law.

I appreciate that there are those here whose personal beliefs – whose faith – makes my father's choice unacceptable. I respect those beliefs. Live your life by them, but do not impose them on others. Let people have the choice at the end of their lives. Allow them dignity in dying as we would want them to have it in life.[39]

---

39 Hansard, HC Deb, 4 July 2019, vol. 662, cols 1417, 1418.

Research we conducted in 2014 found that an estimated 7 per cent of deaths recorded as suicides or likely suicides in this country involve somebody with a terminal illness.[40] We are currently working with coroners and others to shed more light on this problem.

It's important to note that the American Association of Suicidology (AAS) makes a distinction between assisted dying and what we might understand as suicide: '[Assisted dying] is distinct from the behaviour that has been traditionally and ordinarily described as "suicide", the tragic event our organization works so hard to prevent. Although there may be overlap between the two categories, legal physician assisted deaths should not be considered to be cases of suicide.'[41]

The AAS goes on to list the reasons it has arrived at this view, such as: the marked difference between cutting life short and controlling a death that is imminent; the positive impact that assisted dying can have on the

---

40 'Assisted dying: more than 300 terminally ill people a year committing suicide', *Daily Telegraph*, 15 October 2014.

41 Statement of the American Association of Suicidology, '"Suicide" is not the same as "Physician Aid in Dying"', American Association of Suicidology, 2017.

bereavement of loved ones in comparison to suicides; the presence of safeguards in assisted dying to remove the possibility of impulsivity; the difference between 'self-destruction' and 'self-preservation', with the motives of those who choose assisted dying falling into the latter category; and the social stigma that surrounds suicide, stemming from cultural and religious traditions.

This last point is crucial. There are those who wish to label assisted dying as 'assisted suicide' simply because they know that language has a stigmatising effect. They know that it will hurt.

Where it is legal, people who are assisted to die have their underlying illness recorded on their death certificate. There are numerous reasons for that – such as the accuracy of figures relating to terminal illnesses, which aids research into their causes and treatments – but the primary reason is to respect the points the AAS raises. These are not suicides.

This is not a novel concept. Medical examiners determined that the cause of death of those who jumped from the Twin Towers on 11 September 2001 – referred to by medical examiners as fallers, not jumpers – was homicide. This wasn't without controversy; there are reports of people claiming that anyone who jumped to their deaths that day would go to hell and that not classifying their deaths as suicide was a blasphemous attempt to deny them that fate.

Jack Gentul spoke on the phone to his wife Alayne as smoke started to fill the ninety-seventh floor of the South Tower, which she had climbed to help evacuate her colleagues. She told him she was scared as the smoke started to enter the office through air vents. Her remains were later found sufficiently far away from the rubble of the tower to suggest she had jumped. Jack says he found comfort in this. 'Jumping is something you can choose to do,' he said. 'To be out of the smoke and the heat, to be out in the air, it must have felt like flying.'[42]

This is an extreme example, though the parallels with dying people trying to escape suffering that has been imposed on them against their wishes are clear.

People who have an assisted death do not want to die;

---

42 '"It looked like they were blinded by smoke... they just walked to the edge and fell out." Victims who plummeted from Twin Towers', MailOnline, 11 September 2011.

they want to continue to live, but that option has been taken away from them. Brittany Maynard, who moved from California to Oregon in order to make use of that state's assisted dying legislation following the diagnosis of a brain tumour at the age of twenty-nine, explained this succinctly. Brittany said, 'I don't want to die. If anyone wants to hand me a magical cure that will save my life so that I can have children with my husband … I will take them up on it.'[43]

Brittany shared her story and following her death in 2014, her family vowed to continue to campaign in her honour so that others had the option to escape the suffering Brittany did not want to put herself or her family through. In 2015, California's governor, Jerry Brown, had the option to veto the assisted dying law passed by the legislature, and many expected that he would, given his Catholic upbringing. But he did not. Instead he reached an admirable conclusion – one that we believe every politician in the UK has the potential to arrive at, no matter what their current views on assisted dying are.

---

43 'Brittany Maynard: I don't want to die', CNN, 14 October 2014.

In the end, I was left to reflect on what I would want in the face of my own death. I do not know what I would do if I were dying in prolonged and excruciating pain. I am certain, however, that it would be a comfort to be able to consider the options afforded by this bill. And I wouldn't deny that right to others.[44]

Jerry Brown might not have noticed the chains around himself, but he recognised that others could feel theirs.

Starving to death

People can travel overseas to obtain an assisted death, though with great physical, financial, legal and emotional difficulty. People can end their own life in this country, though they risk severe distress for themselves and their loved ones. Often the people who exercise these choices do so alone, without the support of trained professionals, many of whom understandably don't feel they can risk

---

44 'After struggling, Jerry Brown makes assisted suicide legal in California', *LA Times*, 5 October 2015.

their careers, and freedom, by breaking the law, however much empathy they have with the person who is suffering.

However, there is a form of control that is allowed by law but which straddles the blurred line between what is viewed as ethically right and wrong, and clinically acceptable or not. This is euphemistically referred to as VSED (voluntarily stopping eating and drinking), though in effect it means starving or dehydrating oneself to death. To be clear, these are not deaths where a person has lost the ability or willingness to eat or drink in the final few days of their life because of their disease. That is common, but it is quite different from a person making the active choice to hasten their death by weeks or months by refusing food and water.

A palliative care consultant, quoted anonymously in our 'Inescapable Truth' report, questioned this practice: 'I think in the twenty-first century, why are we subjecting someone to such a degrading way of dying? I just find it morally absolutely unacceptable and it shocks me that people, palliative care of all specialties, should put that forward as an option.'

It is shocking, but it does happen. Professor Michael

Rosen founded what is now the Royal College of Anaesthetists. He was an expert in pain management and
developed techniques that allowed patients to control
their own pain relief. Following his death in 2018, *The
Times* described Professor Rosen as a 'pioneer' and a colleague told the *BMJ* that 'he was the most outstanding
anaesthetist in the last half of the twentieth century'.[45]

Professor Rosen was in the end stages of Parkinson's
disease. His daughter Amanda describes his final weeks:

> He was very clear in his mind what he wanted to do. He
> was refusing to eat because he knew he wasn't going to be
> given drugs to die. He knew that he had to stop eating.
>
> It was distressing in the sense that it was clear what he
> wanted to do. He spoke to the consultant and saw her
> on several occasions and she said, 'I can't actively help
> you die; if you are at the point of discomfort, I can ease
> your pain but I can't kill you.' I wanted him to be able
> to discuss it with the palliative care consultant because

---

45 'Obituary: Professor Michael Rosen', *The Times*, 6 June 2018 and 'Michael
Rosen: anaesthetist who championed patients' rights to pain relief', *BMJ*, 3
July 2018.

I didn't want to influence him and I also wanted him to be able to freely talk about what he was feeling. The consultant gave him some sedation to help him to feel more relaxed. But he had to take it in his own hands – to not take calories in, which is a pretty horrible way of dying.

One day I came in to see him and he said, 'Take me to Zurich,' and I said, 'Dad, it's too late, it's too late.' He wanted to end his life. He wanted to be in control. But he was too weak and he was losing control. There's that balance between being weak and having to kill yourself, then being sedated and not being able to have a say in your actions either. There is this interim period where it is actually really terrible.

One of the nurses said, 'We need to ask if he wants his food,' and they brought him a tray of a three-course meal at one point, like a pantomime. He had to be the one to say he didn't want any food. He said, 'Please, I don't want any food.' They said, 'We have to offer it to you every time,' and he found that irritating. Of course he was hungry and he was being presented with food he

didn't want. I think the staff found it incredibly difficult.
I think they were worried about being sued.

It was horrible. He was losing weight. He was uncom-
fortable. He was in the end phase of Parkinson's and he
was starving to death but he was still relatively fit. I said,
'Bad news, Dad. All of those times going to the gym are
not paying off now.'

It took a lot for him to die. He was in an unconscious
state for several days. No fluids, very little urinary output,
obviously declining but his heart was pumping away and
we said, 'How long can this go on for?' In the end it was a
week. I remember saying to the consultant, 'Do you think
I will see you again?' and she said, 'Well, possibly.' She was
very good. She was very caring. She was trying her best.

I just think it was awful he had to starve to death. He
was a very bright, articulate man who knew what he
wanted and had had a good life. He was tired and his Parkinson's was getting worse. He would have preferred to
have said goodbye in an honourable fashion, in control.

I think that is the thing that upset me most of all, he
didn't have the opportunity just to say goodbye, which

would have been very fitting for him. He would have wanted to share his pearls of wisdom once again and then have a very respectable, clean death.

He was 91. For the majority of his life he was an anaesthetist who rose up to be President of the College of Anaesthetists. He was very focused on pain relief and in the early days was involved in pain relief in pregnancy and also palliative care.

He developed patient-controlled analgesia. There was an aphorism he would say to me: 'Never accept for people to be in pain.' That was the irony. His professional life was dedicated to helping others. He had devised something to help others control their pain, yet at the end of life he couldn't take control.

I remember one day he was getting frailer. He was finding it hard to walk to the toilet and he was using a Zimmer frame. I remember him saying, 'I need to walk up and down the corridor. I need to walk up and down the corridor.' He was trying to burn calories. He said, 'It's not happening fast enough.'

He was a truly honourable, moral man and a reflective and very caring man, not only to his family but to patients

throughout his career. He really was hugely respected and
I think to lose your dignity … That wasn't who he was.[46]

Views on terminally ill people starving themselves in
order to accelerate their death are mixed. Some consider it a perfectly acceptable choice that anybody with
mental capacity is free to make. Legally, that is the case.
Many hospices are willing to provide information and
support to terminally ill people exercising this choice,
including pain relief and other treatments to reduce the
severity of symptoms.

In some cases, sedation is offered so that people can
be unconscious and (hopefully) unaware of what is happening. But others question if this practice is ethical and
there are no formal guidelines in place to inform clinicians how and when it should be administered.

Some see choosing to starve to death as a form of suicide, which, as we saw above, can be used to stigmatise
the practice. It is for this reason that many clinicians do
not feel able to support dying people who embark on

---

46 'The Inescapable Truth: How seventeen people a day will suffer as they die',
Dignity in Dying, 2019.

this process, in a similar way that some doctors would refuse to support a patient through an assisted dying request should the law change.

If a dying person is so sure in their mind that they do not want to see out the end stages of their disease that they have the willpower and tenacity to overcome feelings of intense thirst and hunger then why on earth are we prolonging their distress? Why not provide a safe, quick, peaceful means to allow them to escape their pain and die on their terms, to die with their family around them at a time and in a place of their choosing? Why is it preferable to stand back and let people become shells of their former selves who lack the energy to speak or move, let alone say goodbye to and embrace the people they have loved throughout their lives? If those who oppose assisted dying do so on the grounds that it is impossible to protect against pressure and coercion then how are those things mitigated against at present, with this practice? The truth is that they are. We can develop and have developed safeguards and procedures. The problem is that we apply these to practices that are themselves not optimal, and we do so in a way that is entirely dictated by the medical profession. The voice of dying people has, once again, been muffled.

Ethical fudge

An argument we are frequently confronted with is that we do not need to legalise assisted dying because doctors will put us out of our suffering if we ask them to. Of course, you are unlikely to hear it expressed as bluntly as that.

It is rarer for this to happen than it once was, largely because of more stringent regulations around pain relief, introduced following the murders committed by Harold Shipman. While we have heard Shipman's name mentioned in assisted dying debates, it must be reiterated that he murdered people. That could not be further removed from a compassionate doctor responding to an informed request for assistance from a dying person. The idea that an assisted dying law would make it easier for another Shipman ignores the fact that the very reason he was able to commit his crimes was because the safeguards and oversight that assisted dying legislation would provide were not in place.

While Shipman's murders have no doubt made compassionate, but illegal, assistance by doctors more difficult, that is not to say it doesn't still happen. In a 2009 survey, one in thirteen doctors reported that they had made decisions with, to some degree, the intention to hasten a person's death.[47] In a 2019 poll, 62 per cent of healthcare professionals said they believe that there are circumstances in the UK in which doctors or nurses have intentionally hastened death as a compassionate response to a patient's request to end their suffering at the end of life.[48]

The phrase 'out of sight, out of mind' seems apt here. But we would disagree with those who argue it's preferable to leave this practice in the consulting room. There are two issues. Firstly, how can we be confident that what is happening is safe? While we suspect the vast majority – if not all – of those who admit to helping a

47 'Hastening death in end-of-life care: A survey of doctors', *Social Science & Medicine* (2009), vol. 69, no. 11, pp. 1659–66.

48 YouGov, 2019.

patient die do so with good motives, there is no oversight, nor upfront safeguards to this practice. Secondly,
is it fair? The one in thirteen doctors who appear willing to actively hasten death are a minority. It means that
dying people who want the extra option of control face
a lottery. They are fortunate if they happen to be seen
by a doctor who is willing to support their wishes, but
the chances of that are slim. It's also extremely unfair for
doctors who may have to check their natural instincts
to relieve the suffering of their patient at their request
in line with the reality that breaking the law obviously
carries great risks for them.

One of the problems is that doctors themselves recognise that much of end-of-life practice sits in a grey
area. When somebody is near the end of life there is an
unwritten rule in medicine that if pain relief is given
to relieve symptoms, yet the person dies as a result,
then this is OK, both legally and ethically speaking. It
is known as the principle or doctrine of double effect.

There are very few things in life where the intent of
something, as determined by the individual involved, can
result in two such different outcomes: a pat on the back

for good clinical practice or an accusation of murder. This is another aspect of end-of-life care that we must be honest about. Trying to use double effect to resolve the question of assisted dying is nothing less than duplicitous and it is astonishing that anyone expects the public to buy it.

A GP put it much more politely than we can when they said, 'If you are wanting to put an end to someone's misery like that then, really, the best thing is if you can be honest about it and not be trying to do something under another name.'[49]

This comes back to power. Assisted dying challenges a status quo that allows doctors to make the final decision over how someone's life ends. Some doctors appear willing to maintain that system even if it is at best illogical and at worst unsafe, rather than yield that power to their patients.

Shipman might be the most prolific example of unfettered power, but he is not the most absurd. That accolade goes to King George V's doctor. When the king's death was imminent one evening in 1936, his doctor said he

49 'The Inescapable Truth: How seventeen people a day will suffer as they die', Dignity in Dying, 2019.

administered a lethal cocktail of morphine and cocaine to speed things up a little. He believed people should learn of the king's death 'in the morning papers rather than the less appropriate evening journals'.[50]

Regardless of the accuracy of this tale, the fact that there was no public outcry when details of the king's death came to light underlines the fact that there is a cultural acceptance that doctors may sometimes take action to accelerate the dying process. If there was a record of George V actively requesting his death to be hastened, would we think there was anything wrong with it at all? We should trust our moral instincts.

When King George V died, it was illegal to be gay. It was legal for a man to rape his wife. The former did not change until 1967 and the latter, shockingly, was not officially overturned until a ruling by the House of Lords in 1991. Progress in changing the law on these issues was slow, but it was achieved. End-of-life practice has certainly come on since 1936, but it still has a long way to go. It is unacceptable that we are upholding a state

---

50 '1936 Secret is out: Doctor sped George V's death', *New York Times*, 28 November 1986.

of affairs where doctors have control over the fate of mentally competent adults. The ban on assisted dying will be another anachronism consigned to the shameful part of our social history.

Coming back to Shipman, we agree with Professor Aneez Esmail, who was the medical advisor to the Shipman Inquiry. Professor Esmail once opposed assisted dying, but, having in-depth knowledge of the risks of the existing law, he now supports a change in the law:

> Not only do I support the principle of patients having greater autonomy over their death, I also see the potential dangers of doctors having a monopoly on their patients' health. I was the medical advisor to the Shipman Inquiry, a case that exemplified what can happen when a doctor's power goes unchecked. I firmly believe that an assisted dying law with clear safeguards would provide better protections for patients.
>
> Under the status quo, terminally ill patients in the UK are resorting to drastic measures at home and abroad with no protections at all. I don't know how any doctor can be happy to let dying people suffer when palliative

care can no longer help, or turn a blind eye to a patient flying to Switzerland or ending their own lives behind closed doors. Yet if the UK were to introduce legislation similar to Oregon's – which has been in place for over twenty years, and been adopted by nine other US jurisdictions, two Australian states and soon likely New Zealand – we could not only empower our terminally ill patients but also bring the issues involved in doing so out into the open to be properly scrutinised.[51]

Anybody who is concerned about the safety of end-of-life care should support an assisted dying law. Safety comes from transparency, empowerment, fairness and equality. When we do not have those things in place, injustices are allowed to fester. Just because this is the way we are used to doing it does not mean that it should not be challenged.

Sedation

Earlier, Susan Strong described how doctors sedated her

---

51 'If the public supports assisted dying, so should doctors like me', *The Independent*, 25 February 2020.

daughter, Fiona, in the final days of her life. The intention was to remove Fiona's awareness of her pain while she died. Yet because of the fact that the doctors struggled to get the correct dose of sedatives, Fiona regained consciousness numerous times. It was a horrific experience for Fiona and for her family, who will never forget what they witnessed. To quote Haruki Murakami, 'Memories warm you up from the inside. But they also tear you apart.'[52]

People with motor neurone disease who rely on ventilation to stay alive can ask for their ventilation to be removed, and sedation can be administered in an effort to reduce the awareness of what it's like to suffocate to death. However, as Noel Conway wanted to make clear during his court case, no doctor can say for sure what that will feel like, or how long it will take for the person to die, and the person may be robbed of the opportunity to say goodbye to their loved ones in a moment of lucidity. Are we able to draw a moral distinction between a competent, dying adult asking for their ventilation to be removed to bring about their death while

---

52 Haruki Murakami, *Kafka on the Shore* (London: Vintage, 2005).

being sedated, and that same person having the option to self-administer life-ending medication at a time of their choosing?

As flawed as sedation at the end of life is, to the extent that it should never be viewed as a suitable alternative to assisted dying, many dying people would be comforted by knowing that they could request sedation to escape the dying process. The position of the Association for Palliative Medicine prevents a patient-led request for pre-emptive sedation unless there is a specific, clinical need for it, such as Fiona's intractable pain or Noel's anticipated feelings of suffocation.[53] The framework provided by the European Association for Palliative Care (EAPC) states that clinicians should always aim for mild or intermittent sedation in the first instance, i.e. a dosage that allows the person to regain consciousness, or perhaps not even lose consciousness entirely. The practice of what's called continuous deep sedation is considered inappropriate unless the person is in the final hours of their life. The EAPC admits that there is

---

53 'APM position on using sedating medication at the end of life', Association for Palliative Medicine of Great Britain and Ireland, 2009.

no consensus on the appropriateness of sedation when there isn't a specific, intolerable physical symptom to be relieved.[54]

This means that if someone is told they are likely to die in the next two weeks and their pain, nausea and constipation are being managed well, current clinical guidelines – not the law – would likely lead to a doctor denying a person's request to be sedated. But many people, rather than spending a week or more slowly drifting in and out of consciousness, would prefer to be sedated tomorrow lunchtime, once their friends and family have gathered at their bedside in the morning and toasted their life with their favourite drink. Endings matter and many would find great comfort in knowing their story will end with a full stop, or perhaps an ellipsis, rather than an illegible scribble of ink.

The medical profession has written a rulebook for something that most people don't even know is an option. The question of assisted dying needs to be

---

54 'European Association for Palliative Care (EAPC) recommended framework for the use of sedation in palliative care', European Association for Palliative Care, 2009.

answered, but it's not the only one we should ask. We need to examine whether existing practices have been designed to maximise empowerment of the dying person.

❖   ❖   ❖

We think back to Dennis Eccleston and the pain he suffered, both physically because of his disease and existentially because he knew he had no safe option to control his death. He faced this set of miserable choices: continue to suffer; place his faith in care that he knew might reduce the severity of his symptoms but maybe not completely, and possibly not at all; find the money, time, willpower and physical ability to arrange an assisted death overseas; starve himself to death; or rely on a doctor to break the law and jeopardise their career to help him die. When set out like this, his decision to take an overdose and end his own life, with all the risks, loneliness and trauma that entailed, might have appeared to Dennis as the best course of action available to him.

What can we say about a law that allows us to draw that kind of conclusion?

The coronavirus pandemic may have forced us to confront our mortality and prompted us to reassess our relationship with dying, but there have been alarm bells ringing for many years that should have highlighted the unacceptable flaws in our laws and in our culture. These remain, and they will not go away until we commit ourselves to a radically different approach.

Part III

A new vision for dying in the twenty-first century

THE CAMPAIGN FOR assisted dying and the great reforms we have already discussed – votes for women, the expansion of LGBT rights, the advent of patient empowerment – are bound by moral imperatives, yet that is not all. These significant social changes have all been brought to prominence against the backdrop of dramatic moments in history; the shaking up of societal norms allowed voices calling out injustice to be heard more clearly. So, as we now question what our society should look like when it emerges from this current crisis, we must take heed of lessons from the past.

In 1914, at the outbreak of the First World War, Millicent Fawcett issued a rallying cry to women: 'Let us show ourselves worthy of citizenship whether our claim to it be recognised or not.'[55] Women were a central part of the war effort, which created a harmonisation between the suffrage cause and the public mood, and this sowed the seeds for a resolution to women's age-long struggle.

Three years into the war, former Prime Minister Herbert Asquith, a long-time adversary of the suffrage movement, declared in the House of Commons that his views on women's suffrage had changed: 'How could we have carried on the War without them?' he asked. Asquith recognised that society was being transformed and identified this as the ideal opportunity for reform:

> The questions which will then necessarily arise in regard to women's labour and women's functions and activities in the new ordering of things – for, do not doubt it, the old order will be changed – are questions in regard to which I, for my part, feel it impossible, consistently either with justice or with expediency, to withhold from

55 'British women would have waited far longer for the vote without World War I', The Conversation, 6 August 2014.

women the power and the right of making their voice directly heard.[56]

The Representation of the People Act passed in 1918, enfranchising 8.4 million women and 13 million, primarily working-class, men. Ten years later, women were granted the right to vote on the same terms as men. Of course, Fawcett already knew women were worthy of their freedom, just as we know dying people are worthy of theirs. What will it take for politicians to grant it to them?

It is worth highlighting that in the early twentieth century many women in medicine felt unable to speak out in support of the suffrage movement, fearful of what impact expressing a view on a 'controversial' issue of the time might have on their careers.[57] It is a sad reminder of the coerced self-censorship that some palliative care doctors are subjected to today around their views on end-of-life choice. This phenomenon is not new, but

---

56 'Doctors wouldn't let my sister die', BBC News, 10 January 2018 and Hansard, HC Deb, 28 March 1917, vol. 92, cols 469, 470.

57 'IWD 2019: Suffragettes and medical women – examining the "jealous mistress"', Royal College of Physicians, 8 March 2019.

it is as unpleasant and unacceptable now as it was 100 years ago.

In the aftermath of the Second World War, compelled by a unity engendered by a long, traumatic conflict, Britain pursued an ambitious programme of social betterment to eradicate inequality and poverty. Many of the foundations of Britain's welfare state had been laid in the interwar period, yet it was the creation of the NHS in 1948, and the commitment to provide care from cradle to grave free at the point of delivery, that provided the greatest illustration of how death and destruction changed the rules of society. At the end of the First World War, Prime Minister David Lloyd George predicted that peace could lead to 'a new and better age' and presented the challenge 'to make Britain a fit country for heroes to live in'. The creation of the NHS thirty years later can be seen as the ultimate realisation of his vision – though at the time not everyone subscribed to that view. Doctors, many of whom were reluctant to become employees of the state, found themselves lagging behind public opinion on how nationalised healthcare could be implemented, and the government had to carefully navigate the objections of the BMA or otherwise risk seeing its plans scuppered. At the time, a former chairman of the BMA compared the Minister of Health, Aneurin Bevan, to a 'medical Führer' for seeking to nationalise healthcare, a move that he believed would put Britain on a slippery slope to 'the national socialism practised in Germany'.[58] Bevan refused to allow doctors to dictate what society should look like, but he made some concessions to appease them, allowing GP practices to retain their independence and hospital consultants the option to increase their income by providing private medical care should they wish to continue doing so.

Seventy-five years later, the coronavirus pandemic has immortalised the public's love affair with the NHS. How different would this crisis have been if the BMA's opposition to the creation of the NHS had proved too insurmountable and we were robbed of our collective appreciation for that cornerstone of British society? Experience tells us that, while we rightly hold individual doctors in high esteem, we cannot rely on the medical establishment to be at the forefront of progress; it does

---

58 'Making Britain better', BBC News, 1 July 1998.

not always know what is best for us, nor does it possess the understanding, instruments or authority to construct society itself. We have to separate our admiration of individuals, our respect for their collective expertise and dedication, from the necessity of identifying faults in the system in which they operate.

We have seen the need for a more effective culture of planning ahead in day-to-day medicine in order to redress the power imbalance between doctors and the people they care for. Indeed, the BMA now recognises that the ethos of the Mental Capacity Act, which gave legal force to living wills, reflects doctors' obligation to 'respect autonomous decisions made by adults'.[59] Yet the BMA has been on a journey. Before the Act was passed, it had previously supported the principle of allowing patients to refuse treatment in advance of a loss of capacity, though it cautioned against giving people the legal right to do so. A motion tabled for debate at the BMA's annual conference in 1995 warned that refusals of treatment could be considered 'dangerous, open to abuse and incompatible with

59 HL Select Committee, Mental Capacity Act 2005: Oral and written evidence, vol. 1.

the ethical practice of medicine',[60] a precursor to the same inflammatory language some use in the assisted dying debate today. Not least the Christian Medical Fellowship, who also speculated that giving people the right to record their wishes in advance might jeopardise the doctor–patient relationship.[61] This was a development that society as a whole was rightly the arbiter of. And if we accept that that was reasonable, surely the same applies to whether or not we change the law on assisted dying?

Recently updated guidelines from the Faculty of Sexual and Reproductive Healthcare show that medical advice on the contraceptive pill that suggested a seven-day break to allow for natural bleeds was misguided. The recommendation had been in place for the past sixty years. This was partly as a result of efforts to encourage the Catholic Church to deem the contraceptive acceptable and partly because women have not had their needs taken seriously by the medical profession.[62] Many

---

60 HC EDM 1431, 18 July 1995.

61 'Living wills – should we support them?', *Nucleus*, April 1993.

62 'The inventor of the birth control pill designed it to please the Pope – not women', *Glamour*, 22 January 2019.

women still have to find a way to overcome barriers put up by some doctors in order to access the contraceptive pill, the morning-after pill and abortion. Unfortunately, the mantra 'My body, my choice' still depends on having a doctor who does not believe that they have the right to add 'on my terms' to that statement.

Historically, accepted medical practice has favoured sustaining life where possible, if there is no documented evidence to suggest this would not be the person's clear wishes. However, judgments from the Court of Protection in recent years have indicated that the way the law works is evolving, with a clear direction of travel away from the status quo of 'doctor knows best'.[63]

In the case of Paul Briggs, a police officer who suffered a severe brain injury in a motorbike accident, the court was told by doctors that it was in Paul's best interests to continue receiving treatment. They argued that if Paul was moved to a rehabilitation unit, he could regain some decision-making capacity, such as the ability to pick what colour clothes he wanted to wear, though they admitted he

---

63 'Tor Butler-Cole: How Court of Protection judges decide best interests in end of life cases', Medium, 20 October 2017.

would be unlikely to experience any significant increase in physical mobility. The court heard evidence from Paul's wife, Lindsey, who said that she had had conversations with Paul in which he had been clear that he did not believe being kept alive with life-support was 'living'. Lindsey and the rest of Paul's family argued that if he were able to make his views known, he would want treatment to be stopped so he could be allowed to die.

The court sided with Lindsey and Paul's family and ordered the doctors to stop providing life-sustaining treatment and move Paul to palliative care. He died the next month. It was the first case to make clear that a person's wishes, if they could be ascertained reliably, would overrule the views of doctors who might be inclined to preserve life at all costs.

When it comes to assisted dying, recent surveys have highlighted a notable evolution of views amongst doctors. We now recognise that doctors are not fundamentally at odds with the public on this issue, they simply lag behind, just as they have on other elements of end-of-life empowerment, women's rights to autonomy over their bodies and, as noted earlier, even pain relief during childbirth.

We want all doctors to catch up, so we should take inspiration from Aneurin Bevan and allow our moral instincts to carve out a path down which they can follow us.

In 1969, the Stonewall riots lit the touchpaper of LGBT liberation in the USA, yet a decade later the HIV/AIDS epidemic exposed unforgivable neglect of the LGBT community, which had been disproportionately affected by the virus. In the USA, despite deaths from HIV/AIDS rocketing, President Ronald Reagan refused to acknowledge the existence of the epidemic for over five years. His press team joked with journalists about the existence of a 'gay plague'.[64] Out of necessity to survive, pioneering activists took it upon themselves to change the world. Peter Tatchell has described the USA's experience of conquering the HIV/AIDS epidemic as

a tale of triumph over obstructive government, greedy drug companies and homophobic political and religious leaders; transforming a death sentence into a manageable disease – all within the time-frame of a mere decade and

---

64 'The Reagan administration's unearthed response to the AIDS crisis is chilling', *Vanity Fair*, 1 December 2015.

a half. And it was made possible by people with HIV and their LGBT activist allies who dared to question medical, scientific, pharmaceutical and government authority.[65]

The impact of these efforts went beyond taming a virus. The experience allowed LGBT activists to hold a mirror to society and force it to confront the harm that had been inflicted on groups abandoned by government and public health strategies. This provided a platform on which a battle for equality in other areas of life could be waged. How many of those who suffered under Reagan's deliberate silence on the HIV/AIDS epidemic could have imagined that a US President would one day utter the words 'I think same-sex couples should be able to get married'?[66]

By their nature, campaigns to promote human rights frequently interlock, so it is perhaps unsurprising that the HIV/AIDS epidemic was also a catalyst for movements promoting greater choice at the end of life. A

---

65 'A matter of life and death', *The Spectator*, 21 January 2017.
66 'Robin Roberts ABC News interview with President Obama: Obama announced that he now supports same-sex marriage', ABC News, 10 May 2012.

1990 study of doctors in the Netherlands estimated that between 10 and 20 per cent of terminal AIDS patients had been assisted to die.[67] Barbara Coombs Lee, a Herculean activist for patient choice and the president of the US campaign group Compassion & Choices, once reflected on those who helped found her organisation by saying:

> These were people who were on the front lines at the height of the AIDS epidemic. People whom they loved and people whom they served were jumping from balconies and using guns and doing all manner of horrific things to avoid the terrible death that they had witnessed their partners or their loved ones endure.[68]

In 1992, the *San Francisco Chronicle* reported on the death of Steven Shiflett, a man dying of HIV/AIDS who had made a plan to end his own life, with a plastic bag and an overdose, when the symptoms he was experiencing

---

67 Jody B. Gabel, 'Release from terminal suffering? The impact of AIDS on medically assisted suicide legislation', *Florida State University Law Review* (1995), vol. 22, pp. 369–441.

68 'The evolution of America's right-to-die movement', PBS *Frontline*, 13 November 2012.

– chronic diarrhoea, fatigue and an inability to consume anything more substantial than a teaspoon of olive oil – became too much for him to withstand. When enacted, the plan failed and his friends, who were present to attend Steven's 'living wake', called Steven's doctor, who provided instructions on how to administer further medication that would bring about Steven's death. The doctor later said, 'When I hung up the phone, I thought, "Oh my God, I just helped kill somebody." But Steven was going to be dead in a week or two. Steven was looking to shorten his death, not to shorten his life."'[69] Steven's cause of death was recorded as 'AIDS and other infections', just as Alayne Gentul's death on 9/11 was homicide not suicide.

If Steven had been terminally ill in present-day California, he could have had an assisted death under the End of Life Choices Act, the one passed by Governor Jerry Brown in 2015. Neither Steven nor his friends would have had to endure the anxiety and trauma of a DIY death, and his doctor would never have needed to question the legality of his actions. Perhaps Steven

---

69 'One man's choice! Assisted suicide didn't turn out as AIDS patient planned', *San Francisco Chronicle*, 19 October 1992.

might have died like artist Betsy Davis, who, in 2016, dying from motor neurone disease, held a two-day-long celebration of her life with friends before consuming life-ending medication while watching the sunset from her mountainside home in southern California. 'What Betsy did', one of her friends said, 'gave her the most beautiful death that any person could ever wish for.'[70]

The lesson here is that violent wayposts in history can give a voice to grassroots movements. They can expose society's wrongdoings and jolt them into becoming fairer, more egalitarian and more compassionate places to live, in the same way that defibrillators can ameliorate wayward heartbeats, in the right circumstances. So, in the wake of a pandemic that has indiscriminately changed all our lives, we have an opportunity to build ourselves a better world, an opportunity to emancipate freedoms we have previously, inexplicably, caged.

Progress is unstoppable, which is why medical norms once considered sacrosanct, such as doctors being able to override the wishes of their patients, have been shown

---

70 'Terminally ill artist who chose assisted dying gathered friends to say goodbye', *The Guardian*, 12 August 2016.

to bend and ultimately break. We should be suspicious of those who claim that for some miraculous reason we have now arrived at the optimal moment in history where all that came before is good and all that might come next is bad, especially when the people who make this claim have fought progress at every turn.

Dying people have been demanding greater control over how their lives end for decades, but they have been ignored. What better time than now to reassess the status quo, when our way of dealing with death and dying has been revealed as so dysfunctional? We can carefully examine if, as a vocal minority has always argued, it is actually defensible to condemn a significant number of people to suffer as they die. Is that the society we still want to live in, or are we ready to adopt an approach that so many others around the world have already taken?

Assisted dying has been available in Oregon since 1997. The legislation, the Death with Dignity Act, was actually passed in 1994 following a public ballot, but those who fundamentally opposed the Act challenged it in the courts before it came into effect. The compromise offered by the US Supreme Court was to hold another referendum, in which the percentage of those supporting change rose. A lesson, perhaps, for those whose current motivations are to frustrate and delay the process of law change. People will not be fooled, and history will not look kindly on you.

Remember the safe, peaceful, curated deaths that Francie and Charlie Emerick were able to have? Oregon's law works. There have been no cases of abuse; no widening of the eligibility criteria (which are used as the basis for what is proposed in the UK); none of the apocalyptic consequences that were predicted prior to the law being introduced in 1997. The death rate in Oregon has not rocketed; those who have been assisted to die would, as Steven Shiflett's doctor recognised, have died within a few weeks or months with or without an assisted dying law in place.

Celebrating twenty years of the law coming into effect, one local journalist said, 'Death With Dignity is part of how the state defines itself: as pioneering, stubbornly independent and deeply compassionate.'[71]

Lawmakers in Oregon who voted against the law now

---

71 'The true story of how Oregonians won the bitter battle for the right to die', *Willamette Week*, 31 October 2017.

wish that they had supported it. In our years of campaigning, having met people from all over the world, we haven't come across a single person who has been on the opposite journey.

Oregon is not a one-off. Its modest, carefully drafted law has been adopted by nine other US states at the time of writing. It formed the basis of laws recently implemented in two states in Australia, others look set to follow suit. The Parliament of New Zealand passed a similar bill, which is due to be put to a public referendum in 2020. Elements of Oregon's law have been replicated in legislation that now exists in the Netherlands, Belgium, Luxembourg and more recently Canada. Some of these jurisdictions have implemented, from the outset, broader laws than those that exist in the USA and the Antipodes and that which is proposed here. Yet it remains true to say that over 150 million people live in places where they can access meaningful choice at the end of their lives.

These are not reckless jurisdictions. These are places that have had the courage to acknowledge the limits of medicine, and the foresight to develop new strategies to cope with the difficulties of the dying process.

They haven't been prepared to turn their backs on dying people or fold their arms and claim there can't be any other options on the table. More and more assisted dying laws are being passed around the world. None are being repealed. Why? The case for change grows as more countries make progress, yet the arguments put forward to block change stay the same.

Assisted deaths account for less than 1 per cent of deaths in Oregon. This means that Francie, Charlie and 1,655 others have died on their own terms, instead of having the manner of their deaths dictated to them. But many, many more have benefited from the law. Think of all the families who are not haunted, like Emil is, by the memories of watching their loved one suffer. Think of all the doctors, nurses and probably thousands of other healthcare professionals who have not felt trapped by their inability to provide any meaningful relief of suffering to their patients.

Think of all the dying people in Oregon who have benefited from the law existing without ever coming into contact with it. As the former governor of Oregon Barbara Roberts has said, 'Many [Oregonians] simply want to know that, if it gets so bad that they can't tolerate it, the choice is there for them. There is a comfort in knowing it's there.'[72]

Doctors feel that the law has empowered them to have more open and honest conversations about end-of-life care and the treatments that will be available for people. Having these conversations has given doctors more confidence in dealing with issues such as pain relief, assessing capacity and making referrals to hospice care.[73] Are these not improvements we would like to see here?

Assisted deaths don't, therefore, happen because of an absence of good care. Ninety per cent of those who have an assisted death are enrolled in hospice care, for which Oregon is ranked amongst the best in the US.[74] The Oregon Hospice and Palliative Care Association once opposed law change but has since recognised that Oregonians should be supported in whatever choices they want to exercise at the end of their lives, and it quickly acknowledged how well assisted dying worked

72 'The true story of how Oregonians won the bitter battle for the right to die', *Willamette Week*, 31 October 2017.
73 'Assisted Dying in Oregon: Twenty years of a safe and effective law', Dignity in Dying, 2018.
74 'Death with Dignity Act Annual Reports', Oregon Health Authority, 2019.

in practice.[75] The Oregon Medical Association and Oregon Nurses Association dropped their opposition after coming to similar realisations. If assisted dying can't work in practice, as some claim, then why are these organisations not demanding a return to a status quo akin to what we have in the UK?

This is what dying can look like. The idea that an assisted dying law would put vulnerable people at risk of harm is a fabrication; it ignores the safe practice of assisted dying overseas and the opacity of current end-of-life practices in the UK.

Earlier we highlighted how some deflect the assisted dying question with demands for greater funding for palliative care. When Victoria passed assisted dying legislation in 2017, the government reviewed palliative care services and provided an extra AU$72 million to increase palliative care beds and access to home-based palliative care.[76] When draft legislation was introduced

---

75 Hospice & Oregon's Death with Dignity Act, Oregon Hospice and Palliative Care Association, accessed August 2019.

76 'Press release: A genuine, compassionate choice for Victorians', Premier Dan Andrews, 16 June 2019.

in Western Australia, it was accompanied by a commitment to invest an extra AU$41 million in palliative care projects.[77] A report commissioned by Palliative Care Australia examining assisted dying around the world found 'no evidence to suggest that palliative care sectors were adversely impacted by the introduction of legislation. If anything, in jurisdictions where assisted dying is available, the palliative care sector has further advanced.'[78] Those who argue against assisted dying on the grounds that palliative care is under-resourced are doing the specialty, and dying people, a great disservice by trying to delay something that would in fact be the catalyst to bring about the changes they wish to see.

We cannot sit back and let the world move on without us. We need a new social contract around end-of-life care that is in tune with the values of modern society. That must include the option of assisted dying – but there is more.

---

77 'Press release: Landmark voluntary assisted dying legislation to be introduced', Premier Mark McGowan, 6 August 2019.
78 Aspex Consulting, 'Experience internationally of the legalisation of assisted dying on the palliative care sector', Palliative Care Australia, 2018.

The current system is predicated on the insistence that people approaching death relinquish the control they have had throughout their lives. Any decision-making power they are then given is presented as a bonus. We see this in the fact that the most basic of rights, such as the right to refuse treatment, have had to be fought for.

We are now presented with what can only be described as proxy actions of control. Dying at home has somehow become synonymous with a good death, the reason being that if you ask someone where they want to die, they will say, 'At home.' But if you go on to ask people what really matters to them as they die, where they die is not anywhere near as high a priority as being pain-free, being able to make decisions and being lucid and able to say goodbye to family and friends. The unpleasant irony is that dying can require specialist, frequent care. Shifting this into people's homes can increase the likelihood of an unpleasant death. It's as if the system is trying to work towards something it doesn't understand. That's why we end up with piecemeal progress when what is needed is a more fundamental culture shift.

Why can't a dying person demand sedation? Why

can't people be trusted to understand the harsh, grim realities of what dying can be like, alongside the best-case scenario we would all hope for? Why can't we provide a better option than starving and dehydrating yourself to death? Why does the murky grey area of double effect, which makes deities of doctors, still exist? Why can't these decisions be discussed explicitly with dying people, instead of communicated in euphemisms, nods and winks or, worse still, not at all?

Rather than skirting around these issues, we need to address them head on and reframe dying so that it is understood through the gaze of the dying person themselves. If someone approaching the end of their life does not feel in control of their death then clinicians should seek to address this just as they would if their patient presented with pain, nausea or a fever.

The treatment can be pre-emptive. People should be encouraged to plan for their deaths. Every interaction with a clinician should prompt a review of people's end-of-life wishes. Of course, some people may not want to discuss this subject, and the consequences of that should be explained and ultimately respected, but not providing the option to plan ahead should be viewed as clinical negligence, in the same way that withholding pain relief would be.

The treatment can be reactive. People must be given the option of knowing as much detail as they would like about their illness, how it might unfold, what their prognosis might be and, crucially, what might happen to them as they die. These are the building blocks of control; to deny them to people is disempowering. We have to move away from idealised, sanitised, nursery-rhyme accounts of what death can be like, towards truthful, no bullshit, plain-spoken explanations of what could happen, and of course the support and care that will be provided. If somebody doesn't want to know the truth then that is their choice and it should be respected, but we cannot make that choice for society as a whole. The bowdlerisation of death only serves to disenfranchise the dying. We want clarity throughout our lives in our interactions with banks, mobile phone companies, employers, politicians; why not at the end of life? We must move away from the patronising assumption that people facing death are willing to be deceived.

'Nobody told me it would be like this.' That's what the sister of one of our supporters said as she lay in a hospice bed dying in agony as gangrene had developed in one of her hands.[79] She had been promised that she would have the peaceful, pain-free, comfortable death we are told is normal. Not allowing people to prepare for what their death might be like is an abuse of power.

If people are committed to truly improving end-of-life care in this country then these things need to be part of the conversation. So too does the option of assisted dying. If, when confronted with honest information about their deaths, dying people would rather take matters into their own hands then we should find a way to enable that.

As discussed earlier in this book, much has changed about the way we die. Part of this evolution has involved challenging what were once accepted norms underpinning the culture around end-of-life care. That's why we – as a society, not as subjects of medicine – must continue to examine things such as sedation and double effect, and the intent and content of conversations between dying

79 'The Inescapable Truth: How seventeen people a day will suffer as they die', Dignity in Dying, 2019.

people and their doctors, and question whether they need changing. Rather than mount a last-ditch effort to defend the current law, the medical establishment should acknowledge that, as with many other issues that have come before, it might have got assisted dying wrong. Doctors can then work with Parliament to learn from other jurisdictions and implement a safeguarded, compassionate law. This would not, as some have suggested, 'medicalise' death. It would have the opposite effect. It would free dying people from the chains that a culture of paternalism in medicine has unjustifiably restrained them with. Decisions about assisted dying are not there for doctors to make. When the law is changed, it will be a decision for individuals, with doctors who choose to be involved playing a crucial role in safeguarding the process, as they currently do in other aspects of end-of-life care. Until the law changes, doctors have no right to dictate the outcome of the debate.

These things might seem so obvious that it makes no sense to you why dying people cannot have choice and control. That's good. The issue of choice at the end of life is often presented as complex and that is how many people wriggle out of expressing what they really think about the matter, what their instincts tell them. It is not complex. It's very simple. We must respect the person who is dying. We must provide them with what they need to have the death they want.

Complexity is what happens under the current law. Complexity is a doctor deciding whether or not they want to risk their career by responding to their patient's request for help. Complexity is the lonely preparation process of a dying person who wants to end their own life with the most certainty and least mess and before their wife returns home so that she is not implicated in a crime. Complexity is trying to disguise a planned death at Dignitas as a restful city break in Zurich. Complexity arises when one is tasked with justifying why the Ecclestons and the Emericks had such vastly different experiences of dying.

There is a better, simpler way and there has never been a more fitting time to implement it.

We will end by quoting the fearless and peerless Sir Terry Pratchett. Terry was a patron of Dignity in Dying and he once observed that his success was owed to the fact that his readers were like drops of mercury; while initially disparate, with time they found each other, coalesced, and formed a blob greater than the sum of its parts. This unified force then had the power to influence others. He anticipated that the same would happen for our campaign, and it has. Terry told us that 'generations stream away and people change and things thought of as totally impossible suddenly turn out to be everyday'. Soon assisted dying will be legal. Fifty years ago, few would have dreamed that law change was possible. Twenty years ago, it would still have been considered radical. Now we find ourselves on the precipice of change. The public will is resolute. Evidence of the current law's failings is indisputable. Other countries have shown us how it can be done. The rules that determine how we die have been exposed as cruel, contradictory and out of touch. It is time to rewrite them.

Afterword by Molly Meacher, Chair of Dignity in Dying

THIS BOOK MAKES clear why one of the most popular policies being debated in the UK is the right of dying people to decide when to end their suffering. We have to consider why this human right has not yet been honoured in the UK when countries and states are reforming the law elsewhere.

When we are dying, our fate is entirely in doctors' hands. We are denied a say over how and when we die. The result is that every year more than 300 dying people in Britain take their lives in dangerous and traumatic ways,[80] and multiples of that number attempt to do so

---

80 'Assisted dying: more than 300 terminally ill people a year committing suicide', *Daily Telegraph*, 15 October 2014.

and fail. Every year, about fifty of us go to Switzerland to find a dignified death, albeit far from home and at great risk to their loved ones;[81] and even with access to the very best care, every year more than 6,000 of us will die having suffered unnecessarily, because dying patients have no safe and legal choice to avoid an unbearable death.[82]

The great majority of the population want our law changed so that if they are facing death, they can choose when their suffering has become unbearable and be helped to end it. The fact is we all want some control over how we die. We want to avoid the risk of choking to death or suffering unbearably in other ways before we die. Many of us have known a loved one who has suffered terribly before dying. We would all live more happily if we knew we would be able to die well.

At the moment, all doctors are prohibited from helping us out of our misery, no matter how compassionate

---

81 'The True Cost: How the UK outsources death to Dignitas', Dignity in Dying, 2017.
82 'The Inescapable Truth: How seventeen people a day will suffer as they die', Dignity in Dying, 2019.

their motives. They risk fourteen years in prison if they take the risk, not to mention being struck off. The best doctors will do all they can to alleviate suffering, but we have created a culture around end-of-life care where dying people do not always feel able to discuss their preferences for how they want to die.

Only Parliament can change the law. Our politicians need to understand that 84 per cent of the public will support them if they vote for assisted dying to be legalised.[83] Most importantly, we have seen a massive shift in the support of doctors for a law change. The Royal College of Physicians and the Royal College of GPs held surveys of their members which showed majorities supporting a move away from opposition by their colleges.[84] Both colleges saw a huge surge in the number of doctors who now believe their representative bodies should support a change in the law.

In addition, the great majority of disabled people also want the right to an assisted death. Their most ardently

---

83 Populus, 2019.

84 'Press release: No majority view on assisted dying moves RCP position to neutral', Royal College of Physicians, March 2019.

opposed self-appointed spokespeople don't reflect the views of the section of society they purport to represent. Similarly, the majority of religious people in this country also support assisted dying.[85] Only a minority of Christians, but most faith leaders, deny that dying people have autonomy and free will to decide over their own deaths. I respect those beliefs, but it is important that they are not imposed upon others with different religious beliefs or none. The British public will be on the side of every politician who votes for a change in the law and for the right of each one of us to an assisted death when we are terminally ill if we are mentally competent to make the decision for ourselves.

Much has been made of the risk to vulnerable people. But if we are serious about those concerns, we must accept that the hypothetical heartless relation can, under the existing laws, subtly encourage an elderly person to bring their life to an end through starvation and dehydration or ceasing treatment. If assisted dying were legalised, far greater safeguards would be in place than there are at present.

---

85 Populus, 2019.

We need proper information about how the current law is working. What are the good things about it and what are the problems with it? There is strong support for an inquiry into the operation of the current law prohibiting assisted dying. When the coronavirus crisis abates, we hope that a select committee will take on this task. It will of course be a matter to be decided by the committee itself. Parliament owes it to us all to examine the suffering under the current law and whether or not a new right to assisted dying should be introduced.

The fight for the rights of dying people stands as the latest in a fine tradition of crusades for moral reforms including the rights of enslaved people, women and LGBT people. The way the coronavirus pandemic has changed our relationship with death has provided the context. Politicians now need to conclude the reform of our age.

"I have looked after patients who had a good death but also witnessed patients who suffered unimaginably despite our best efforts at palliative care. How we die should not be a lottery, and this book is a call for justice and choice. Every doctor, whether they agree with assisted dying or not, should try to understand why dignity in death should be right for all of us."

DR ANEEZ ESMAIL, PROFESSOR OF GENERAL PRACTICE AT THE UNIVERSITY OF MANCHESTER, MEDICAL ADVISOR TO THE SHIPMAN INQUIRY 2000–05

"This book has never been more important. The Covid-19 pandemic has given many of us a sense of our own mortality. And while many people can, often with the help of our extraordinary palliative care professionals, 'live until they die', others do not have that privilege. This book puts a powerful argument to afford our citizens the right to leave this world in a place, time and manner of their choosing."

DR SARAH JARVIS, GP, BROADCASTER AND AUTHOR

"I have been a GP in the East End of London for thirty years. Despite our best efforts, some terminally ill patients suffer and would choose to end their life on their terms. This book sets out how a new law would give them and their families one of the greatest gifts in life, a good death, and why the time for change is now."

PROFESSOR SIR SAM EVERINGTON MBBS MRCGP OBE, BARRISTER AND GP

"As a doctor who sees the full spectrum of what death is, good and bad, this book is a poignant reminder of why our laws need to change. I want every patient and every colleague to read it and see beyond our collective reluctance to talk about the end of life. We only have one chance to get death right for every person – read this, talk to your loved ones, and don't be afraid."

Dr Zoe Norris, GP and whistleblower on sexism at the British Medical Association

"If we defer the question of assisted dying to future generations, they will be astonished at the horror we knowingly subjected dying people to. *Last Rights* sets out the definitive case for why we must now provide people with the option of a peaceful death, surrounded by those they love."

Nell Dunn, author of *Up the Junction* and *Poor Cow*